Dinah Zike's
Reading and Study Skills
for *Glencoe Health*

FOLDABLES™

Glencoe

New York, New York   Columbus, Ohio   Chicago, Illinois   Peoria, Illinois   Woodland Hills, California

The McGraw-Hill Companies

Send all inquiries to:
Glencoe/McGraw-Hill
21600 Oxnard Street, Suite 500
Woodland Hills, California 91367

ISBN: 0-07-861870-3

2 3 4 5 6 7 8 9   079   08 07 06 05

Table of Contents

What's a Foldable?

A Foldable is a three-dimensional, student-made, interactive graphic organizer based on a skill. Making a Foldable gives students a fast, kinesthetic activity that helps them organize and retain information. Every chapter in the Student Edition of the textbook begins with a Foldable that is used as a study organizer. Each chapter's Foldable is designed to be used as a study guide for the main ideas and key points presented in the chapter. Foldables can also be used for a more in-depth investigation of a concept, idea, opinion, event, or person or place studied in a chapter. The purpose of this ancillary is to show you how to create various types of Foldables and provide chapter-specific Foldables examples. With this information, you can individualize Foldables to meet your curriculum needs.

This book is divided into two sections. The first section presents step-by-step instructions, illustrations, and photographs of 34 Foldables, many of which are not used in the Student Edition. I've included over 100 photographs to help you visualize how the Foldables might enhance instruction. The second section presents additional ideas on how to use Foldables for each chapter in the textbook. You can use the instruction section to design your own Foldables or alter the Foldables presented in each chapter. I recommend making this book available as a source for students who wish to learn new and creative ways to make study guides, present projects, or do extra credit work.

Some of the Foldables featured in this book have been used in supplemental programs or staff development workshops. Today my Foldables are used internationally. I present workshops and keynote addresses to over 50,000 teachers and parents each year, sharing Foldables that I began inventing, designing, and adapting over 35 years ago. Students of all ages are using them for daily work, note-taking activities, student-directed projects, forms of alternative assessment, journals, graphs, charts, tables, and more.

Have fun using and adapting Foldables!

Dinah Zike

Why Use Foldables in Health?

When teachers ask me why they should take the time to use the Foldables featured in this book, I explain that Foldables

- quickly organize, display, and arrange data, making it easier for students to grasp health studies concepts, theories, facts, opinions, questions, research, and ideas.

- help sequence events as outlined in the content standards.

- result in study guides the students compile as they listen for main ideas, read for main ideas, or conduct research.

- provide a multitude of creative formats in which students can present projects, research, interviews, and inquiry-based reports instead of typical poster board formats.

- replace teacher-generated writing or photocopied sheets with student-generated print.

- incorporate the use of such skills as comparing and contrasting, recognizing cause and effect, and finding similarities and differences into daily work and long-term projects. For example, these Foldables can be used to compare and contrast student explanations and opinions with explanations and opinions currently accepted by experts in the field of health.

- continue to "immerse" students in previously learned vocabulary, concepts, information, generalizations, ideas, and theories, providing them with a strong foundation that they can build on with new observations, concepts, and knowledge.

- can be used by students or teachers to easily communicate data through graphs, tables, charts, models, and diagrams, including Venn diagrams.

- allow students to make their own journals for recording observations, research information, primary and secondary source data, surveys, and more.

- can be used as alternative assessment tools by teachers to evaluate student progress or by students to evaluate their own progress.

- integrate language arts, science, mathematics, and social studies into the study of health.

- provide a sense of student ownership or investment in the health curriculum.

Foldable Basics

What to Write and Where

Teach students to write general information such as titles, vocabulary words, concepts, questions, main ideas, and dates on the front tabs of their Foldables. This way students can easily recognize main ideas and important concepts. Foldables help students focus on and remember key points without being distracted by other print.

Ask students to write specific information such as supporting ideas, student thoughts, answers to questions, research information, class notes, observations, and definitions under the tabs.

As you teach, demonstrate different ways in which Foldables can be used. Soon you will find that students make their own Foldables and use them independently for study guides and projects.

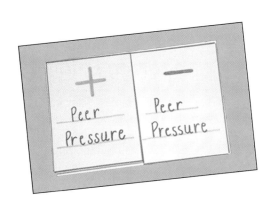

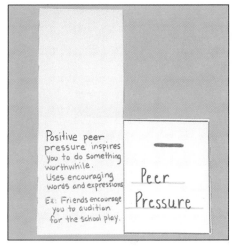

With or Without Tabs

Foldables with flaps or tabs create study guides that students can use to self-check what they know about the general information on the front of tabs. Use Foldables without tabs for assessment purposes or projects where information is presented for others to view quickly.

Venn diagram used as a study guide

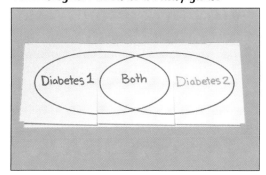

Venn diagram used for assessment

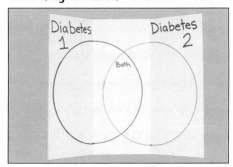

What to Do with Scissors and Glue

If it is difficult for your students to keep glue and scissors at their desks, set up a small table in the classroom and provide several containers of glue, numerous pairs of scissors (sometimes tied to the table), containers of crayons and colored pencils, a stapler, clear tape, and anything else you think students might need to make their Foldables.

Storing Foldables

There are several ways that students can store their Foldables. They can use grocery bags, plastic bags, or shoeboxes. Students can also punch holes in their Foldables and place them in a three-ring binder. Suggest that they place strips of 2″ clear tape along one side and punch three holes through the taped edge.

By keeping all of their Foldables together and organized, students will have created their own portfolio.

HINT: *I found it more convenient to keep student portfolios in my classroom so student work was always available when needed. Giant laundry-soap boxes make good storage containers for portfolios.*

Use This Book As a Creative Resource

Have this book readily available for students to use as an idea reference for projects, discussions, debates, extra credit work, cooperative learning group presentations, and so on. Encourage students to think of their own versions of Foldables to help them learn the material the best way possible.

Basic Foldable Shapes

The following figures illustrate the basic folds that are referred to throughout the following section of this book.

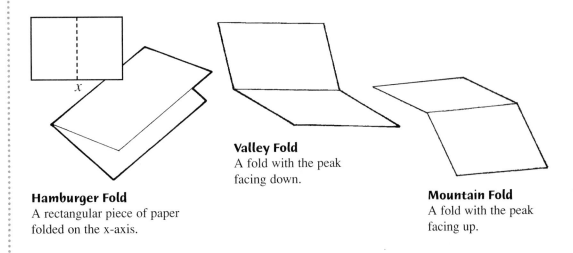

Hamburger Fold
A rectangular piece of paper folded on the x-axis.

Valley Fold
A fold with the peak facing down.

Mountain Fold
A fold with the peak facing up.

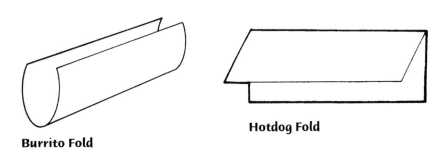

Burrito Fold

Hotdog Fold

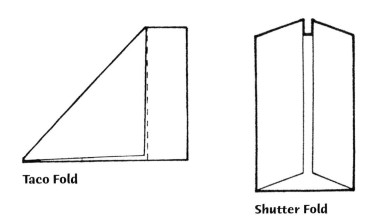

Taco Fold

Shutter Fold

Half-Book

Fold a sheet of paper (8½″ × 11″) in half.

1. This book can be folded vertically like a *hotdog* or . . .

2. . . . it can be folded horizontally like a *hamburger.*

Use this book for descriptive, expository, persuasive, or narrative writing, as well as graphs, diagrams, or charts.

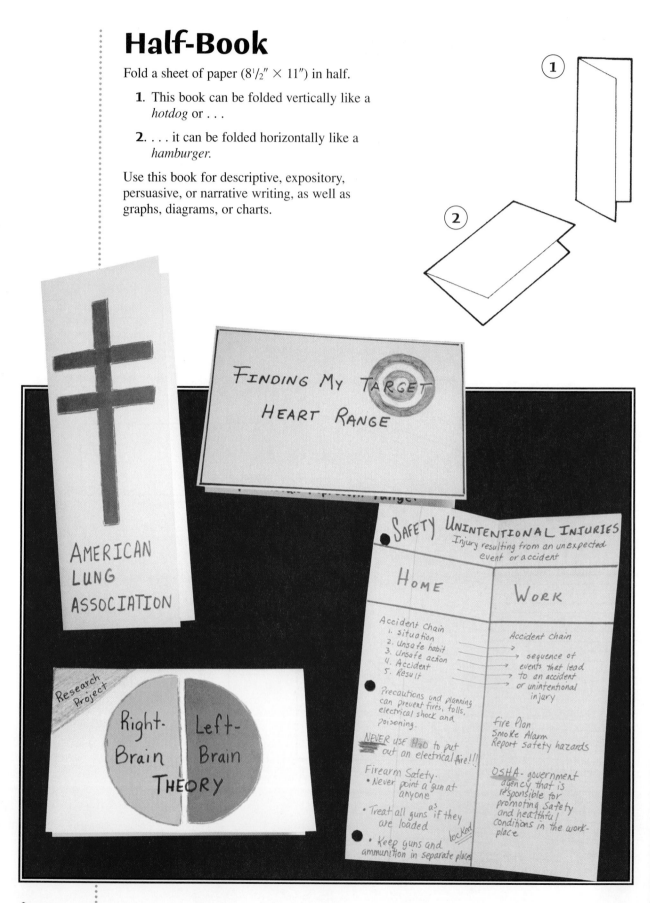

Folded Book

1. Make a *half-book* using the *hamburger* fold.

2. Fold it in half again. This makes a ready-made cover, and two small pages for information on the inside.

Use photocopied work sheets, Internet printouts, and student-drawn diagrams or maps to make this book. One sheet of paper becomes two activities and two grades.

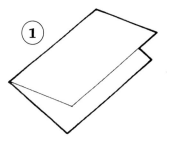

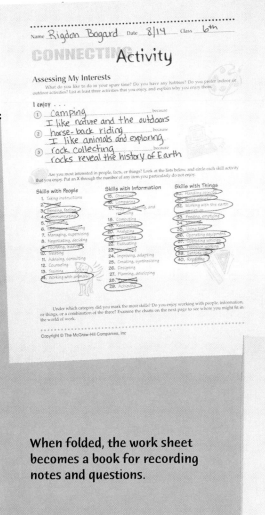

When folded, the work sheet becomes a book for recording notes and questions.

Three-Quarter Book

1. Take a *two-tab* book (page 11) and raise the left-hand tab.

2. Cut the tab off at the top fold line.

3. A larger book of information can be made by gluing several *three-quarter books* side-by-side.

Sketch or glue a graphic to the left, write one or more questions on the right, and record answers and information under the right tab.

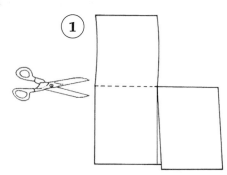

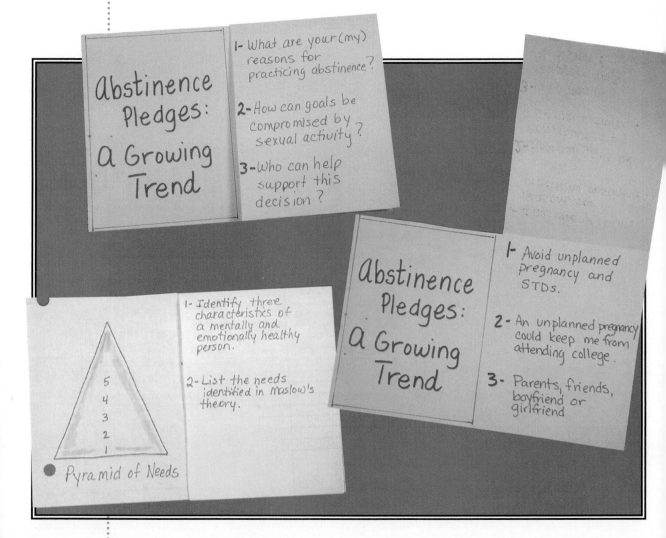

Bound Book

1. Take two sheets of paper ($8\frac{1}{2}'' \times 11''$) and separately fold them like a *hamburger*. Place the papers on top of each other, leaving $\frac{1}{16}''$ of an inch between the *mountain tops*.

2. Mark both folds 1" from the outer edges.

3. On one of the folded sheets, cut along the fold from the top and bottom edge to the marked spot on both sides.

4. On the second folded sheet, start at one of the marked spots and cut the fold between the two marks.

5. Take the cut sheet from Step 3 and fold it like a *burrito*. Place the *burrito* through the other sheet and then open the *burrito*. Fold the bound pages in half to form an eight-page book.

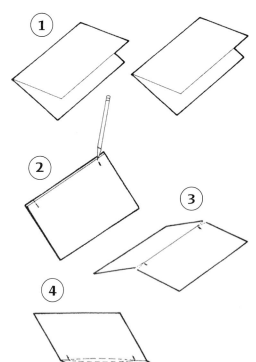

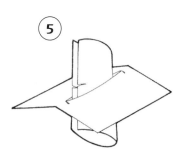

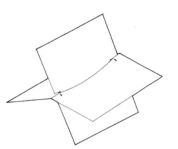

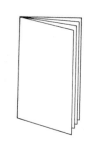

Picture-Frame Book

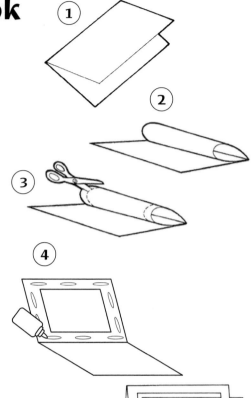

1. Fold a sheet of paper (8½″ × 11″) in half like a *hamburger.*

2. Open the *hamburger* and gently roll one side of the *hamburger* toward the *valley.* Try not to crease the roll.

3. Cut a rectangle out of the middle of the rolled side of the paper leaving a ½″ border, forming a frame.

4. Fold another sheet of paper (8½″ × 11″) in half like a *hamburger.* Apply glue to the inside border of the picture frame and place the folded, uncut sheet of paper inside.

Use this book to feature a person, place, or thing. Inside the picture frames, glue photographs, magazine pictures, computer-generated graphs, or have students sketch pictures. This book has three inside pages for writing and recording notes.

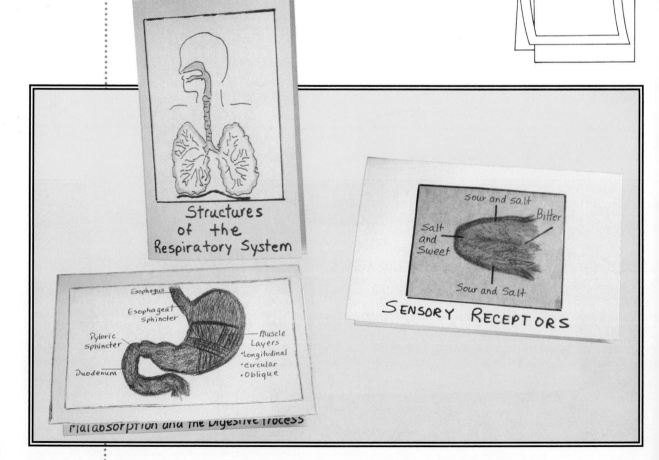

Structures of the Respiratory System

Malabsorption and The Digestive Process

Esophagus
Esophageal Sphincter
Pyloric Sphincter
Duodenum
Muscle Layers
•Longitudinal
•circular
•Oblique

Sour and salt
Bitter
Salt and Sweet
Sour and Salt
SENSORY RECEPTORS

Two-Tab Book

1. Fold a sheet of paper like a *hamburger*, but fold it so that one side is longer. Take a *folded book* and cut up the *valley* of the inside fold toward the *mountain top*. This cut forms two large tabs that can be used front and back for writing and illustrations.

2. The book can be expanded by making several of these folded books and gluing them inside of each other.

Use this book with data occurring in twos. For example, use it for comparing and contrasting, determining cause and effect, finding similarities and differences, and more.

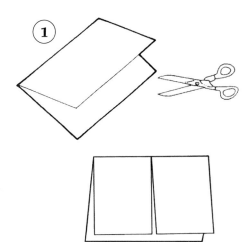

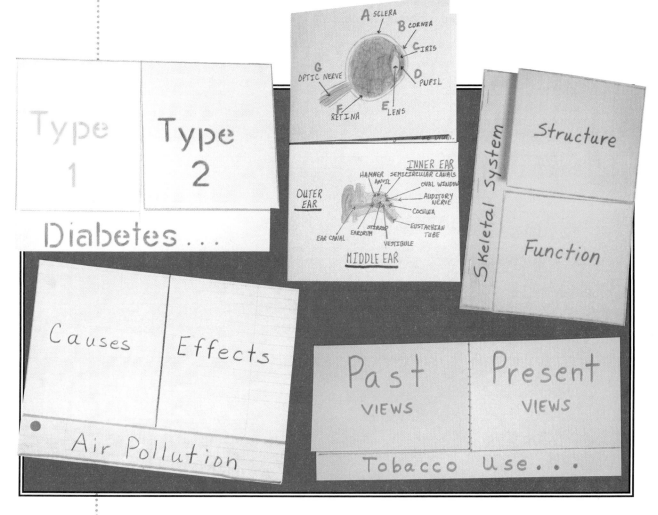

Pocket Book

1. Fold a sheet of paper ($8\frac{1}{2}'' \times 11''$) in half like a *hamburger*.

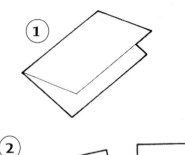

2. Open the folded paper and fold one of the long sides up 2″ to form a pocket. Refold along the *hamburger* fold so that the newly formed pockets are on the inside.

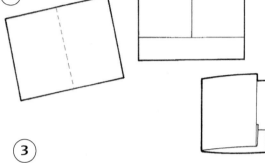

3. Glue the outer edges of the 2″ fold with a small amount of glue.

4. **Optional:** Glue a cover around the *pocket book.*

   Variation: Make a multipage booklet by gluing several pockets side-by-side. Glue a cover around the multipage *pocket book.*

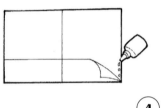

Use $3'' \times 5''$ index cards and quarter-sheets of notebook paper inside the pockets. Store student-made books, such as two-tab books and folded books, in the pockets.

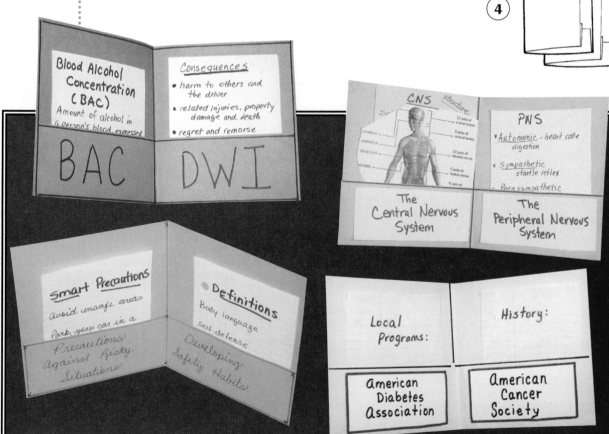

Matchbook

1. Fold a sheet of paper ($8\frac{1}{2}" \times 11"$) like a *hamburger,* but fold it so that one side is 1″ longer than the other side.

2. Fold the 1″ tab over the short side forming an envelope-like fold.

3. *Optional*: Cut the front flap in half toward the *mountain top* to create two flaps.

Use this book to report on one thing, such as one person, place, or thing, or for reporting on two things, such as the cause and effect of water pollution.

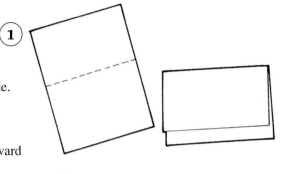

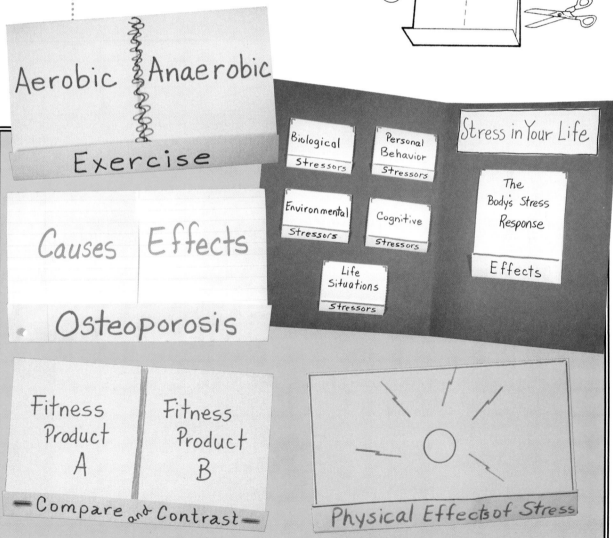

Shutter Fold Book

1. Begin as if you were going to make a *hamburger*, but instead of creasing the paper, pinch it to show the midpoint.

2. Fold the outer edges of the paper to meet at the pinch, or midpoint, forming a *shutter fold*.

Use this book for data occurring in twos. Or, make this fold using 11″ × 17″ paper, and smaller books—such as the *half book*, *journal*, and *two-tab book*—can be glued inside to create a large project full of student work.

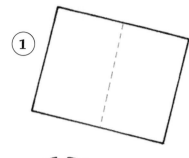

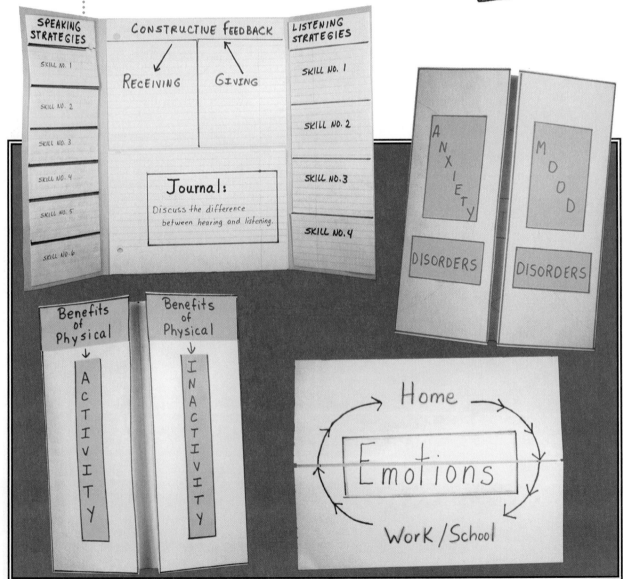

Forward-Backward Book

1. Stack three or more sheets of paper. On the top sheet trace a large circle.

2. With the papers still stacked, cut out the circles.

3. Staple the paper circles together along the left-hand side to create a book.

4. Label the cover and take notes on the pages that are on the right.

5. Turn the book over and label the back. Takes notes on the pages that are on the right.

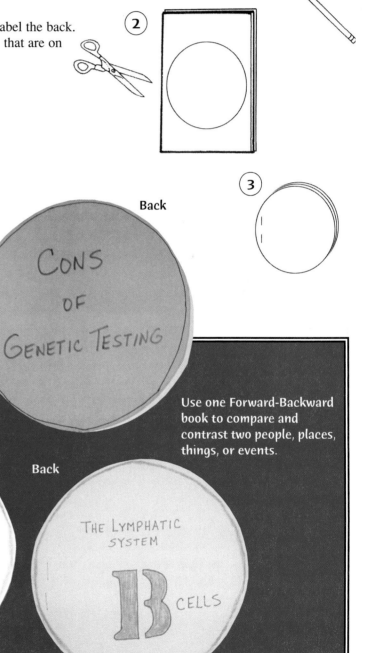

Front

Back

PROS OF GENETIC TESTING

CONS OF GENETIC TESTING

Use one Forward-Backward book to compare and contrast two people, places, things, or events.

Front

Back

THE LYMPHATIC SYSTEM

T CELLS

THE LYMPHATIC SYSTEM

B CELLS

Three-Tab Book

1. Fold a sheet of paper like a *hotdog*.

2. With the paper horizontal, and the fold of the *hotdog* up, fold the right side toward the center, trying to cover one-half of the paper.

   NOTE: *If you fold the right edge over first, the final graphic organizer will open and close like a book.*

3. Fold the left side over the right side to make a book with three folds.

4. Open the folded book. Place your hands between the two thicknesses of paper and cut up the two *valleys* on one side only. This will form three tabs.

Use this book for data occurring in threes, and for two-part Venn diagrams. To create a tab, fold so that one side is longer in Step 1.

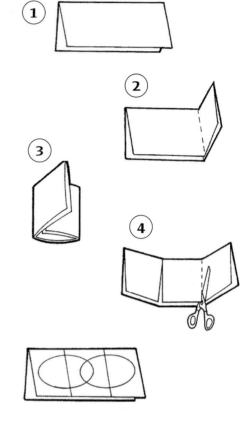

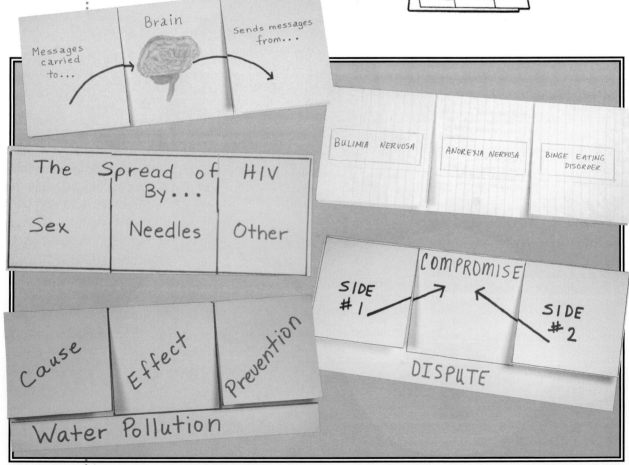

Three-Tab Book Variations

VARIATION A:
Draw overlapping circles on the three tabs to make a Venn diagram.

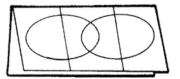

VARIATION B:
Cut each of the three tabs in half to make a six-tab book.

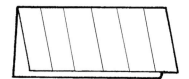

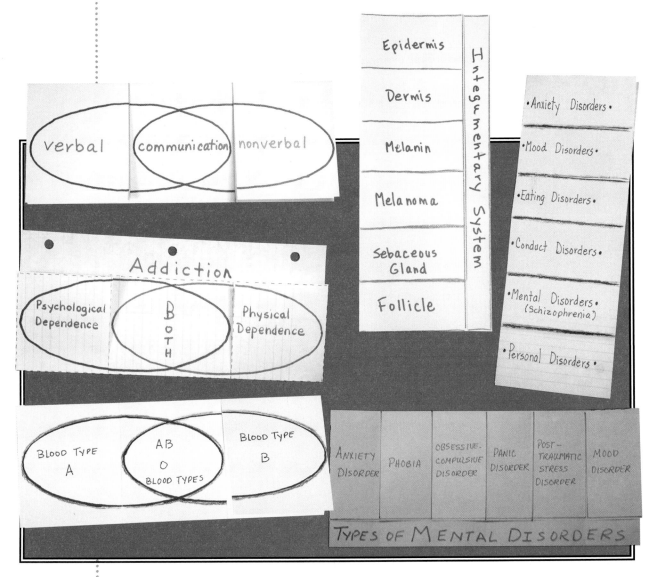

Pyramid Fold

1. Fold a sheet of paper (8½″ × 11″) into a *taco*. Cut off the excess rectangular tab formed by the fold.

2. Open the folded *taco* and refold it the opposite way forming another *taco* and an X-fold pattern.

3. Cut one of the folds to the center of the X, or the midpoint, and stop. This forms two triangular-shaped flaps.

4. Glue one of the flaps under the other, forming a *pyramid*.

5. Label front sections and write information, notes, thoughts, and questions inside the pyramid on the back of the appropriate tab.

Use to make mobiles and dioramas.

Use with data occurring in threes.

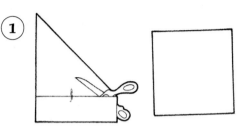

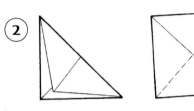

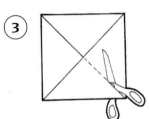

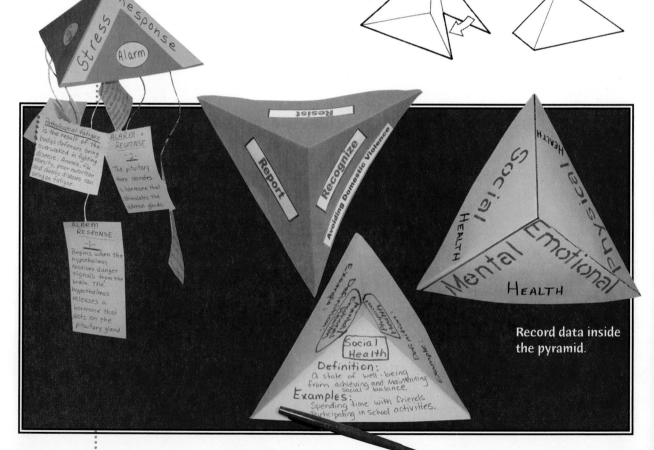

Record data inside the pyramid.

Tri-fold Book

1. Fold a sheet of paper (8½″ × 11″) into thirds.

2. Use this book as is, or cut into shapes. If the tri-fold is cut, leave plenty of fold on both sides of the designed shape so the book will open and close in three sections.

Use this book to make charts with three columns or rows, large Venn diagrams, reports on data occurring in threes, or to show the outside and inside of something and to write about it.

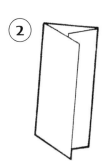

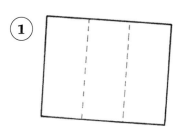

INNER EAR
(Labyrinth)

Semicircular canals
three bony, fluid-
filled loops, involved
in the sense of
balance

cochlear nerve
acoustic nerve

vestibule
passageway,
entry, controls balance

cochlea
small bone, area of
hearing, coiled 2½
times into the shape
of a snail

Eustachian tube- connects
nose/throat to ear, equalizes
air pressure.

MIDDLE EAR

Malleus-one of
three tiny bones,
resembles a hammer,
connected to the
ear drum, carries
vibrations to the
incus

Incus one of three
tiny bones, also
called the anvil,
communicates sound
vibrations

Stapes one of three
tiny bones, resembles
a small stirrup, carries
vibrations

Ear drum-tympanic
membrane

OUTER EAR

Auricle channels
sound waves

External auditory
canal
passageway about one
inch long that leads
to the outer ear and the
ear drum, lined with
tiny hairs and glands that
produce wax to protect
the ear

Temporal bone pair of
large bones that form
part of the skull

Mastoid process
projection of the temporal
bone, point of attachment
for muscles

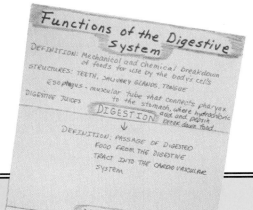

Functions of the Digestive System

DEFINITION: Mechanical and chemical breakdown
of foods for use by the body's cells
STRUCTURES: TEETH, SALIVARY GLANDS, TONGUE
Esophagus - muscular tube that connects pharynx
to the stomach, where hydrochloric
acid and pepsin
break down food.
DIGESTION ↓

DEFINITION: PASSAGE OF DIGESTED
FOOD FROM THE DIGESTIVE
TRACT INTO THE CARDIOVASCULAR
SYSTEM

ABSORPTION ↓

DEFINITION: EXPULSION OF UNDIGESTED
FOOD OR BODY WASTES
Pancreas produces digestive enzymes that are
carried to the small intestine. Amylase, trypsin,
and lipase breakdown carbs, proteins and ...
ELIMINATION

👓 EYE CARE 👓

Training: College
Medical School
specialized training

Opthalmologists

Training: college
Medical School

Optometrists

Training: short-term
training

Opticians

M.D.
Work: Specializes
in the medical
and surgical
care of the eyes
and visual system

O.D.
Work: doctor of
optometry who
diagnoses, treats
and manages diseases
of the visual system.

Work: technician who
provides technical
and patient
services

LYMPHATIC SYSTEM

B CELLS
Stimulated to multiply
when they come in contact with
a pathogen. Some are formed into
plasma cells that produce antibodies.
Other B cells form memory cells that
respond to second exposures to the pathogen.

LYMPHOCYTES
Specialized white blood
cells that provide the
body with immunity

Stimulated to enlarge and multiply
in response to a pathogen. Killer T cells
stop the spread of disease by releasing
toxins. Helper T cells aid the actions
of B cells and T cells.

T CELLS

Three-Pocket Book

1. Fold a sheet of paper (11″ × 17″) into thirds vertically.

2. Fold the bottom edge up 2″ and crease well. Glue the outer edges of the 2″ tab to create three pockets.

3. Label each pocket. Use to hold notes taken on index cards or quarter-sheets of paper.

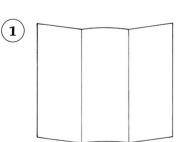

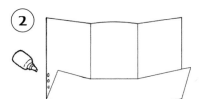

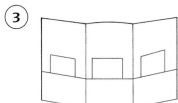

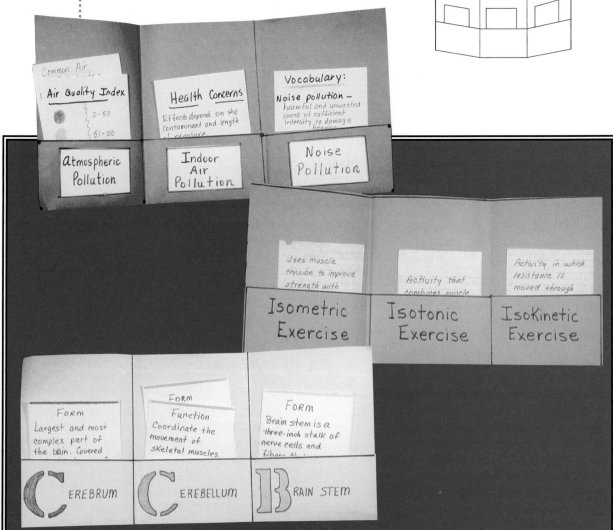

Four-Tab Book

1. Fold a sheet of paper (8½" × 11") in half like a *hotdog*.

2. Fold this long rectangle in half like a *hamburger.*

3. Fold both ends back to touch the *mountain top* or fold it like an *accordion.*

4. On the side with two *valleys* and one *mountain top,* make vertical cuts through the top sheet of paper, forming four tabs.

Use this book for data occurring in fours, such as skin, nails, hair, and teeth.

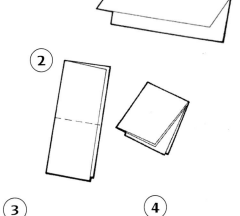

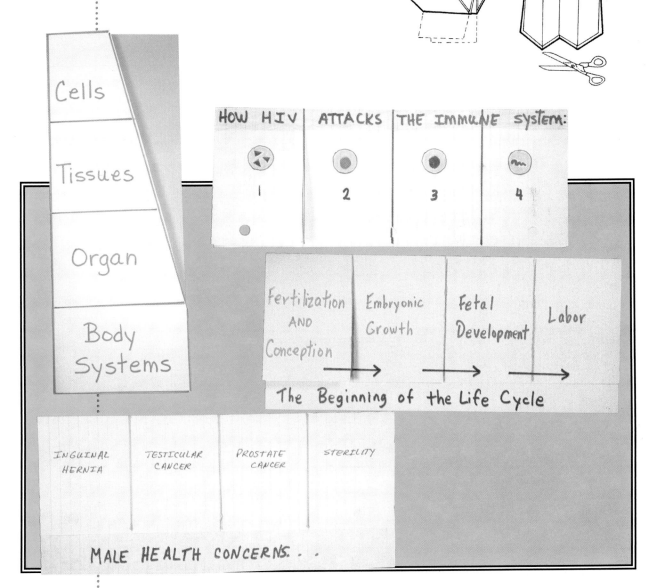

Cells

Tissues

Organ

Body Systems

HOW HIV | ATTACKS | THE IMMUNE system:

1   2   3   4

Fertilization AND Conception | Embryonic Growth | Fetal Development | Labor

The Beginning of the Life Cycle

INGUINAL HERNIA | TESTICULAR CANCER | PROSTATE CANCER | STERILITY

MALE HEALTH CONCERNS. . .

Standing Cube

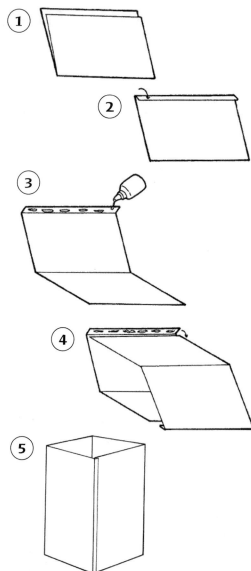

1. Use two sheets of the same size paper. Fold each like a *hamburger*. However, fold one side ¹/₂″ shorter than the other side. This will make a tab that extends out ¹/₂″ on one side.

2. Fold the long side over the short side of both sheets of paper, making tabs.

3. On one of the folded papers, place a small amount of glue along the the small folded tab, next to the *valley* but not in it.

4. Place the non-folded edge of the second sheet of paper square into the *valley* and fold the glue-covered tab over this sheet of paper. Press flat until the glue holds. Repeat with the other side.

5. Allow the glue to dry completely before continuing. After the glue has dried, the cube can be collapsed flat to allow students to work at their desks. The cube can also be folded into fourths for easier storage, or for moving it to a display area.

Use with data occurring in fours or make it into a project. Make a small display cube using 8¹/₂″ × 11″ paper. Use 11″ × 17″ paper to make large project cubes that you can glue other books onto for display. Notebook paper, photocopied sheets, magazine pictures, and current events also can be displayed on the large cube.

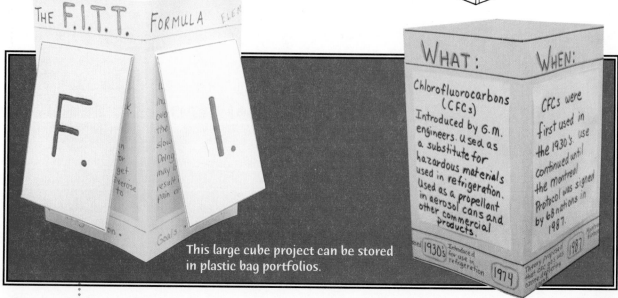

This large cube project can be stored in plastic bag portfolios.

Four-Door Book

1. Make a *shutter fold* using 11″ × 17″ or 12″ × 18″ paper.

2. Fold the *shutter fold* in half like a *hamburger.* Crease well.

3. Open the project and cut along the two inside *valley* folds.

4. These cuts will form four doors on the inside of the project.

Use this fold for data occurring in fours. When folded in half like a *hamburger,* a finished *four-door book* can be glued inside a large (11″ × 17″) *shutter fold* as part of a larger project.

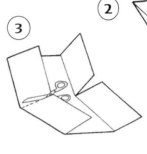

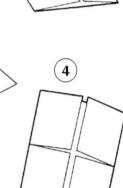

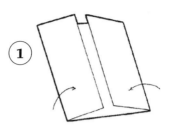

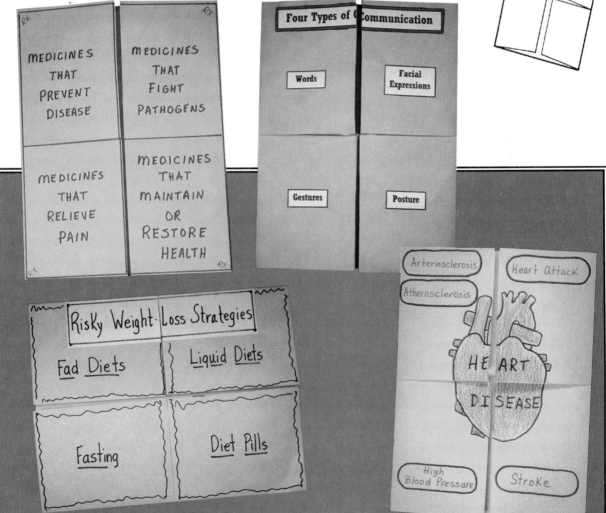

Envelope Fold

1. Fold a sheet of paper ($8\frac{1}{2}'' \times 11''$) into a *taco*. Cut off the excess paper strip.

2. Open the folded *taco* and refold it the opposite way, forming another *taco* and an X-fold pattern.

3. Open the *taco* and fold the corners toward the center point of the X, forming a small square.

4. Trace this square on another sheet of paper. Cut and glue it to the inside of the envelope. Pictures can be placed under or on top of the tabs, or can be used to teach fractional parts.

Use this book for data occurring in fours, such as infancy, childhood, adolescence, and adulthood.

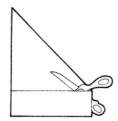

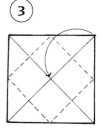

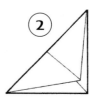

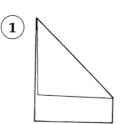

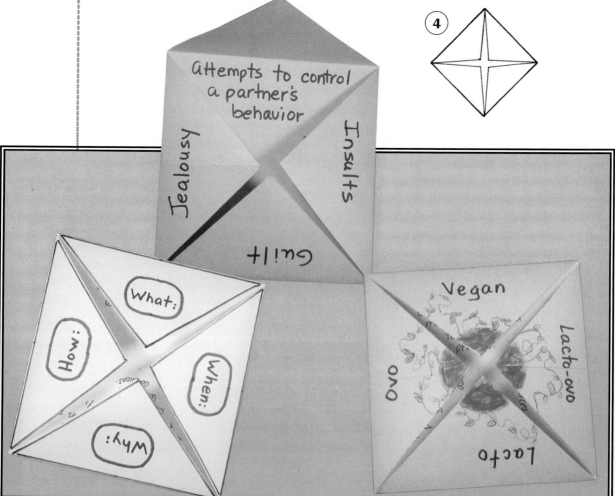

Layered-Look Book

1. Stack two sheets of paper ($8\frac{1}{2}'' \times 11''$) so that the back sheet is 1″ higher than the front sheet.

2. Bring the bottom of both sheets upward and align the edges so that all of the layers or tabs are the same distance apart.

3. When all tabs are an equal distance apart, fold the papers and crease well.

4. Open the papers and glue them together along the *valley* or inner center fold or staple them along the *mountain*.

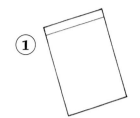

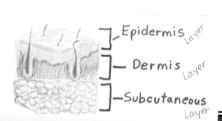

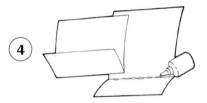

Physical
LEVEL 1

Safety
LEVEL 2

Belonging
LEVEL 3

Feeling Recognized
LEVEL 4

Reaching Potential
LEVEL 5

Your
Mental + Emotional
Health

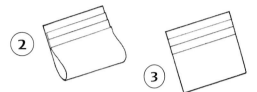

Epidermis Layer

Dermis Layer

Subcutaneous Layer

SKIN

• Illegal Drugs •

• Stimulants •

• Depressants •

• Narcotics •

• Hallucinogens •

• Inhalants •

• Marijuana •

• Anabolic Steroids •

Communicable Diseases

- Causes -

- Transmission -

- Prevention -

When using more than two sheets of paper, make the tabs smaller than 1″.

Top-Tab Book

1. Fold a sheet of paper ($8\frac{1}{2}'' \times 11''$) in half like a *hamburger.* Cut the center fold, forming two half-sheets.

2. Fold one of the half-sheets four times. Begin by folding in half like a *hamburger*, fold again like a *hamburger* three more times. This folding has formed your pattern of four rows and four columns, or 16 small squares.

3. Fold two sheets of paper ($8\frac{1}{2}'' \times 11''$) in half like a *hamburger.* Cut the center folds, forming four half-sheets.

4. Hold the pattern vertically and place a half-sheet of paper under the pattern. Cut the bottom right-hand square out of both sheets. Set this first page aside.

5. Take a second half-sheet of paper and place it under the pattern. Cut the first and second right-hand squares out of both sheets. Place the second page on top of the first page.

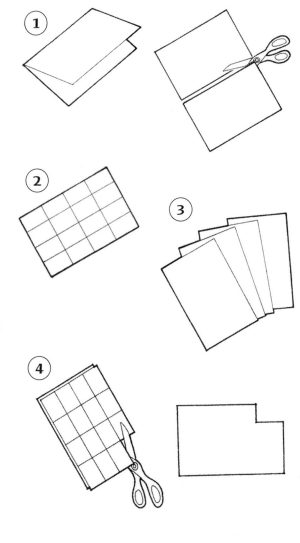

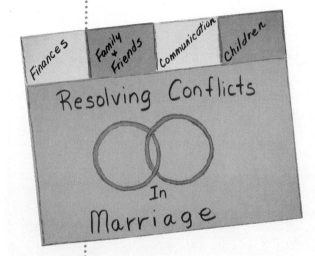

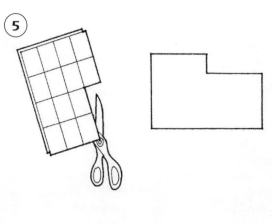

6. Take a third half-sheet of paper and place it under the pattern. Cut the first, second, and third right-hand squares out of both sheets. Place this third page on top of the second page.

7. Place the fourth, uncut half-sheet of paper behind the three cutout sheets, leaving four aligned tabs across the top of the book. Staple several times on the left side. You can also place glue along the left paper edges, and stack them together. The glued spine is very strong.

8. Cut a final half-sheet of paper with no tabs and staple along the left side to form a cover.

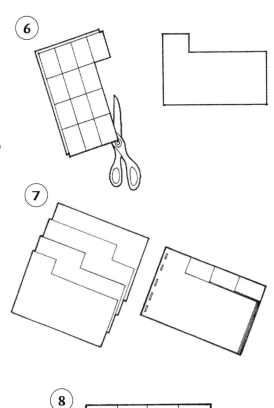

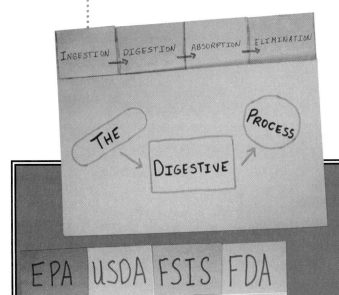

INGESTION DIGESTION ABSORPTION ELIMINATION

THE → DIGESTIVE → PROCESS

EPA USDA FSIS FDA

HEALTH SERVICES
AT THE
NATIONAL LEVEL

Cardio Endurance Muscle Strength Muscle Endurance Flexibility

Elements
of
Fitness

Folding a Circle into Tenths

1. Fold a paper circle in half.

2. Fold the half-circle so that one-third is exposed and two-thirds are covered.

3. Fold the one-third (single thickness) section backward to form a fold line.

4. Fold the two-thirds section in half.

5. The half-circle will be divided into fifths. When opened, the circle will be divided into tenths.

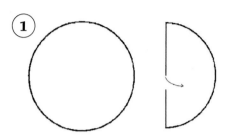

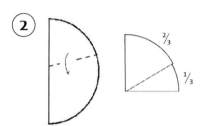

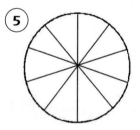

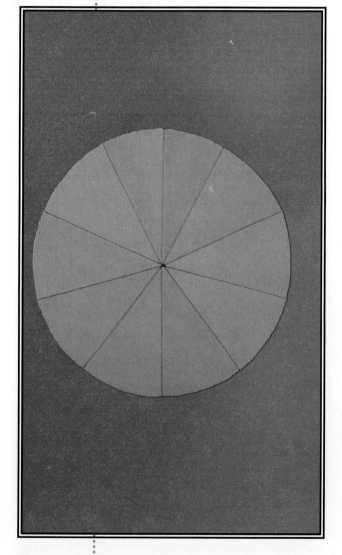

NOTE: *Paper squares and rectangles are folded into tenths the same way. Fold them so that one-third is exposed and two-thirds are covered. Continue with Steps 3 and 4.*

Circle Graph

1. Cut out two circles using a pattern.

2. Fold one of the circles in half on each axis, forming fourths. Cut along one of the fold lines (the radius) to the middle of each circle. Flatten the circle.

3. Slip the two circles together along the cuts until they overlap completely.

4. Spin one of the circles while holding the other stationary. Estimate how much of each of the two circles should be exposed to illustrate given percentages or fractional parts of data. Add circles to represent more than two percentages.

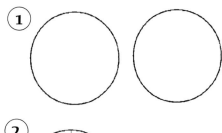

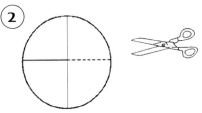

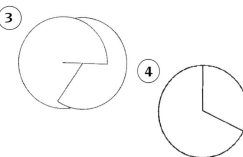

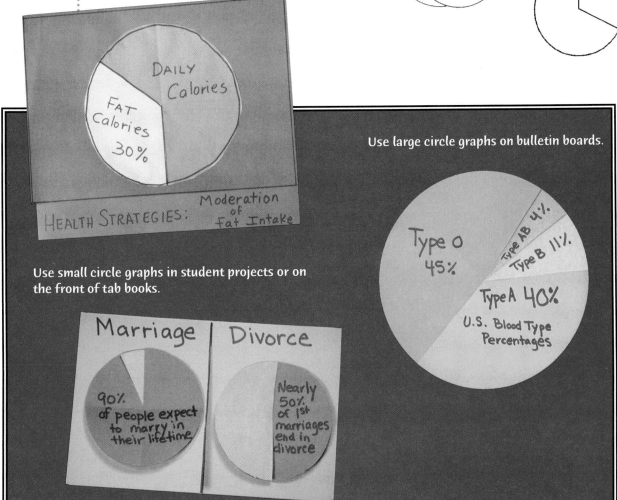

DAILY Calories

FAT Calories 30%

HEALTH STRATEGIES: Moderation of Fat Intake

Use large circle graphs on bulletin boards.

Type O 45%

Type AB 4%
Type B 11%
Type A 40%

U.S. Blood Type Percentages

Use small circle graphs in student projects or on the front of tab books.

Marriage | Divorce

90% of people expect to marry in their lifetime

Nearly 50% of 1st marriages end in divorce

Folding into Fifths

1. Fold a sheet of paper in half like a *hotdog* or *hamburger* for a five-tab book, but fold it so that one side is longer. Leave open for a folded table or chart.

2. Fold the paper so that one-third is exposed and two-thirds are covered.

3. Fold the two-thirds section in half.

4. Fold the one-third section (single thickness) backward to form a fold line.

The paper will be divided into fifths when opened.

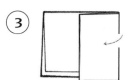

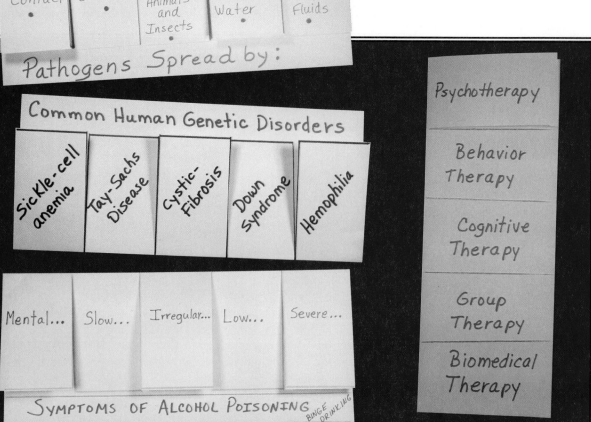

Folded Table or Chart

1. Fold the number of vertical columns needed to make the table or chart.

2. Fold the horizontal rows needed to make the table or chart.

3. Label the rows and columns.

Remember: Tables are organized along vertical and horizontal axes, while charts are organized along one axis, either horizontal or vertical.

Table

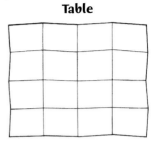

Chart

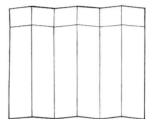

Human Papillomavirus (Genital Warts)	Chlamydia	Genital Herpes	Gonorrhea	Trichomoniasis	Syphilis
Incidence: 5.5 million. Prevalence: 20 million. Most common STD in the US. CDC estimates that 50-75% of sexually active males and females acquire HPV at some point. Almost all cases of cervical cancer are caused by HPV. Genital warts may appear one to three months after infection. Virus can be treated but not cured.	Incidence: 3 million. Prevalence: 2 million. Bacterial infection. 40% of cases reported in teens 15-19 years old. Symptoms include penis discharge, burning during urination, females have vaginal discharge, burning, and pain in abdomen. Can be treated with antibiotics but person can become infected again. Can cause sterility, PID, chronic pelvic pain, and premature birth.	Incidence: 1 million. Prevalence: 45 million. Type 1- cold sores. Type 2- genital sores. About 20% of adolescent population is infected. Causes blisterlike sores. Can be transmitted in absence of symptoms. Medication can relieve symptoms but not cure virus. Potentially fatal to infants and may increase chances of contracting AIDS.	Incidence: 650,000. Prevalence: Not Available. Bacterial STD that usually affects mucous membranes. Symptoms in males: discharge from penis, painful urination. Symptoms in females: vaginal discharge, odor, painful urination. About 50% of all cases are asymptomatic. Can be treated with antibiotics. Gonorrhea can cause joint damage and blindness in infants.	Incidence: 5 million. Prevalence: Not available. Caused by a microscopic protozoan. Female symptoms may include vaginal discharge, odor, irritation, itching. Males usually show no symptoms and are generally treated when the female partner is infected.	Incidence: 70,000. Prevalence: 417,000. Caused by a small bacterium called a spirochete. First sign of infection is a painless, red sore called a chancre. The sore will heal but the infection will pass to the heart, liver, nervous system, and kidneys. Paralysis, convulsions, blindness, and heart disease can result. Can be passed to unborn fetuses.

	+ EFFECTS	— EFFECTS
PEERS AND FRIENDS		
PHYSICAL HEALTH	Motivate to join an athletic team. Participate in healthy activities like hiking, biking, or swimming.	Promote use of tobacco, alcohol, or other drugs. Encourage sexual promiscuity or risky activities. Engage in physical violence.
MENTAL/EMOTIONAL HEALTH	Are loyal. Offer support and encouragement. Show respect.	Bully. Harass. Tease. Manipulate. Pressure.
SOCIAL HEALTH	Encourage involvement in helping the community. Discussing world events. Motivate to join a team. Introduce to other friends.	Pressure to participate in illegal activities. Dictate what is "cool" and "uncool" despite how you feel.

Tobacco	Tobacco products include cigarettes, cigars, pipes, smokeless tobacco and bidis. Smoke contains more than 4,000 chemicals and 43 cause cancer. Nicotine, tar, and carbon monoxide are harmful substances found in tobacco.
Smokeless Tobacco	Smokeless tobacco is not used like cigarettes. It is chewed, inhaled or held in the mouth. Substances in chewing tobacco and snuff mix with saliva and come in contact with tissues in the mouth, throat and stomach if swallowed.
Second-Hand Smoke	Tobacco smoke that stays in the air and inhaled by nonsmokers can cause some of the same health problems found in smokers. More than 40,000 nonsmokers die each year from secondhand smoke. Serious health problems are found in children under 18 months old that are exposed to secondhand smoke.

Accordion Book

NOTE: *Steps 1 and 2 should be done only if paper is too large to begin with.*

1. Fold the selected paper into *hamburgers*.

2. Cut the paper in half along the fold lines.

3. Fold each section of paper into *hamburgers*. However, fold one side ¹/₂″ shorter than the other side. This will form a tab that is ¹/₂″ long.

4. Fold this tab forward over the shorter side, and then fold it back away from the shorter piece of paper (in other words, fold it the opposite way).

5. Glue together to form an *accordion* by gluing a straight edge of one section into the *valley* of another section.

NOTE: *Stand the sections on end to form an* accordion *to help students visualize how to glue them together. (See illustration 5.)*

Always place the extra tab at the back of the book so you can add more pages later.

Use this book for time lines, student projects that grow, sequencing events or data, and biographies.

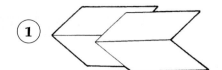
1

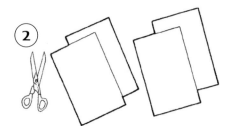
2

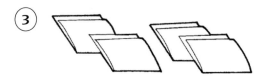
3

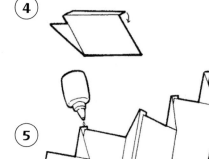
4

5

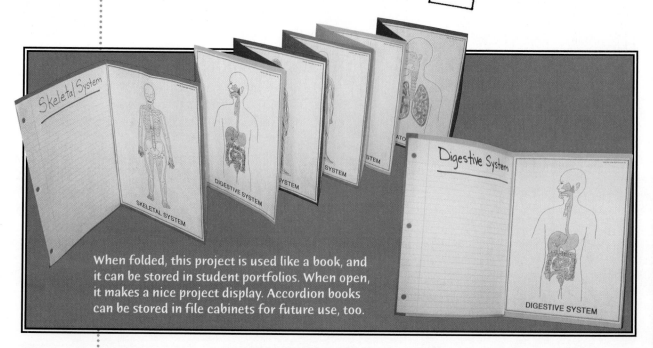

When folded, this project is used like a book, and it can be stored in student portfolios. When open, it makes a nice project display. Accordion books can be stored in file cabinets for future use, too.

Pop-Up Book

1. Fold a sheet of paper (8½″ × 11″) in half like a *hamburger.*

2. Beginning at the fold, or *mountain top,* cut one or more tabs.

3. Fold the tabs back and forth several times until there is a good fold line formed.

4. Partially open the *hamburger* fold and push the tabs through to the inside.

5. With one small dot of glue, glue figures for the *pop-up book* to the front of each tab. Allow the glue to dry before going on to the next step.

6. Make a cover for the book by folding another sheet of paper in half like a *hamburger.* Place glue around the outside edges of the *pop-up book* and firmly press inside the *hamburger* cover.

Option: Use the tabs, cut at different lengths, to make pop-up bar graphs.

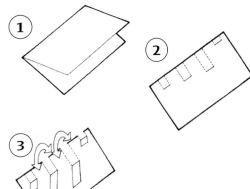

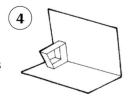

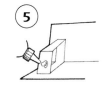

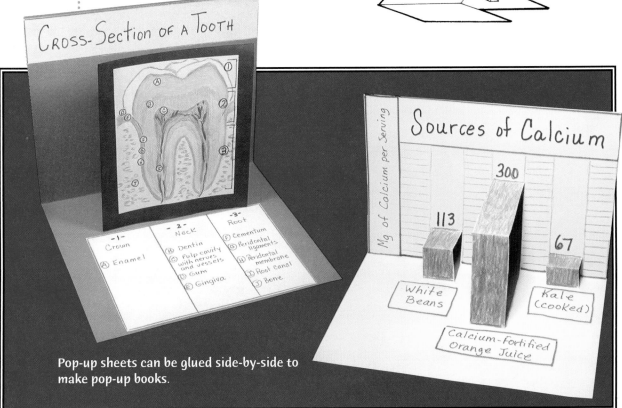

Pop-up sheets can be glued side-by-side to make pop-up books.

Four-Door Diorama

1. Make a *four-door book* out of a *shutter fold*.

2. Fold the two inside corners back to the outer edges (*mountains*) of the *shutter fold*. This will result in two *tacos* that will make the *four-door book* look like it has a shirt collar. Do the same thing to the bottom of the *four-door book*. When finished, four small triangular *tacos* have been made.

3. Fold the book in half to form a 90-degree angle and overlap the folded triangles to make a display case that doesn't use staples or glue. (It can be collapsed for storage.)

4. Or, as illustrated, cut off all four triangles, or *tacos*. Staple or glue the sides.

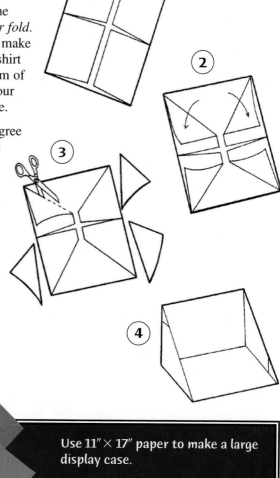

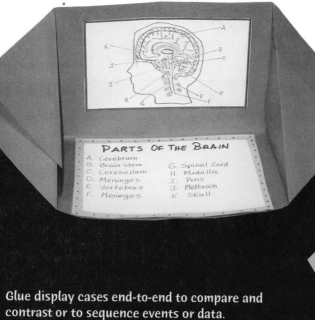

Use 11″ × 17″ paper to make a large display case.

Use poster board to make giant display cases.

Glue display cases end-to-end to compare and contrast or to sequence events or data.

Concept-Map Book

1. Fold a sheet of paper along the long or short axis, leaving a 2″ tab uncovered along the top.

2. Fold in half or in thirds.

3. Unfold and cut along the two or three inside fold lines.

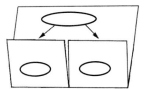

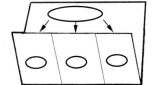

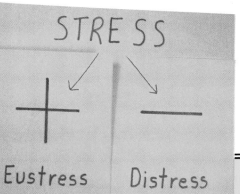

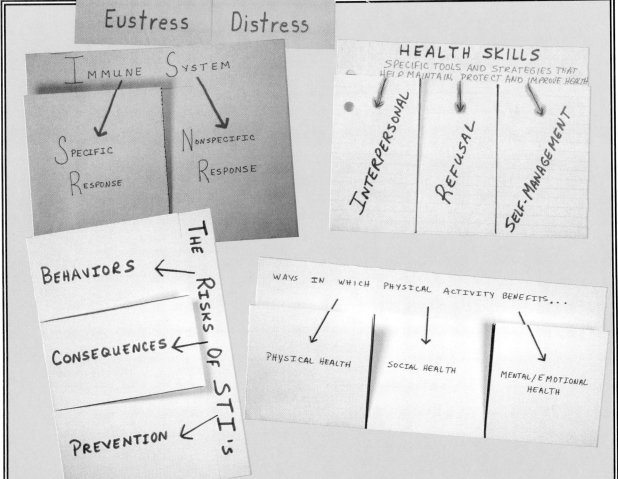

Project Board with Tabs

1. Decide how many tabs you will need and where their locations will be. Lightly draw them on the board.

2. Pinch and slightly fold the paper at the point where a tab is desired on the illustrated project board. Cut into the paper on the fold. Cut straight in, then cut up to form an "L." When the paper is unfolded, it will form a tab with an illustration on the front.

3. After all tabs have been cut, glue this front sheet onto a second piece of paper. Place glue around all four edges and in the middle, away from tabs. Add illustrations and text to the board and under the tabs.

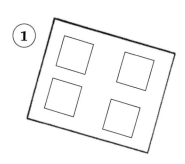

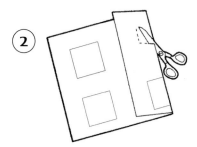

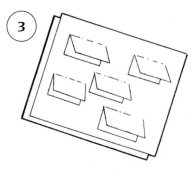

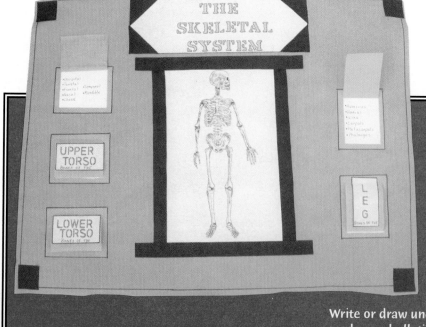

Write or draw under the tabs. If the project is made as a bulletin board using butcher paper, quarter- and half-sheets of paper can be glued under the tabs.

Billboard Project

1. Fold all pieces of the same size of paper in half like *hamburgers*.

2. Place a line of glue at the top and bottom of one side of each folded billboard section and glue them edge-to-edge on a background paper or project board. If glued correctly, all doors will open from right to left.

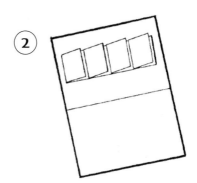

3. Pictures, dates, words, and so on, go on the front of each billboard section. When opened, writing or drawings can be seen on the inside left of each section. The base, or the part glued to the background, is perfect for more in-depth information or definitions.

Use for time lines or sequencing data, such as the stages of pregnancy or the path of the digestive system.

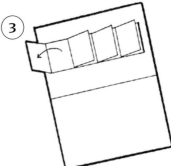

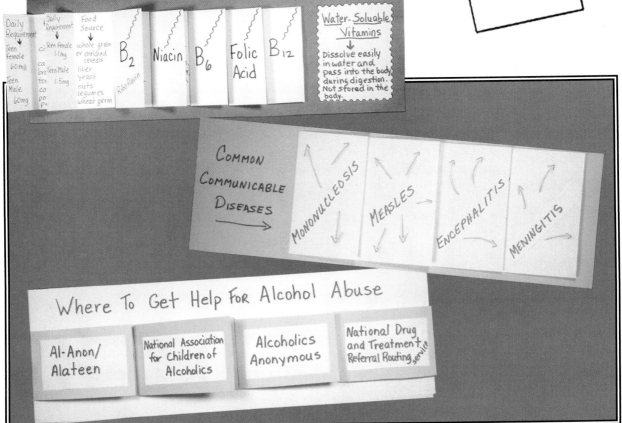

Vocabulary Book

1. Fold a sheet of notebook paper in half like a *hotdog*.

2. On one side, cut every third line. This results in 10 tabs on wide-ruled notebook paper and 12 tabs on college-ruled paper.

3. Label the tabs.

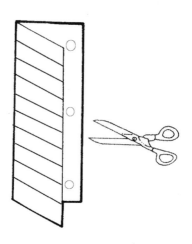

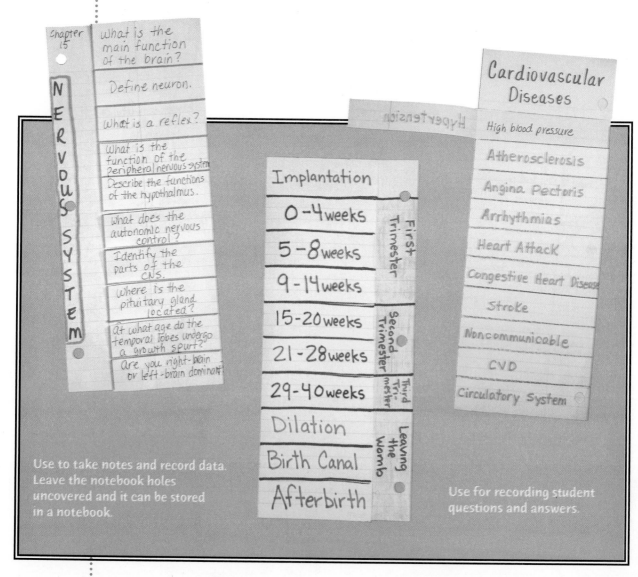

Use to take notes and record data. Leave the notebook holes uncovered and it can be stored in a notebook.

Use for recording student questions and answers.

Sentence Strips

1. Take two sheets of paper (8½″ × 11″) and fold into *hamburgers*. Cut along the fold lines making four half-sheets. *(Use as many half-sheets as necessary for additional pages to your book.)*

2. Fold each sheet in half like a *hotdog*.

3. Place the folds side-by-side and staple them together on the left side.

4. One inch from the stapled edge, cut the front page of each folded section up to the *mountain top*. These cuts form flaps that can be raised and lowered.

To make a half-cover, use a sheet of construction paper 1″ longer than the book. Glue the back of the last sheet to the construction paper strip, leaving 1″ on the left side, to fold over and cover the original staples. Staple this half-cover in place.

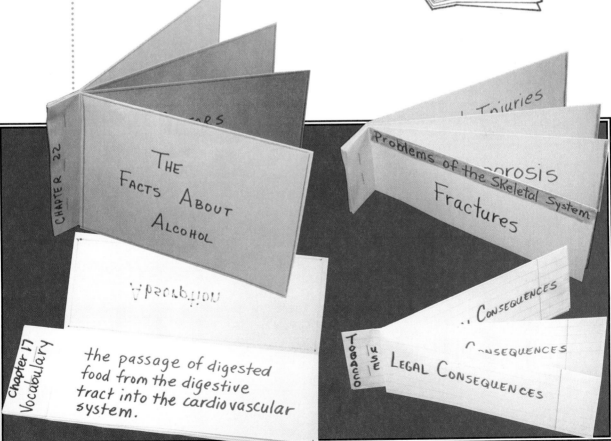

Sentence-Strip Holder

1. Fold a sheet of paper (8½" × 11") in half like a *hamburger*.

2. Open the *hamburger* and fold the two outer edges toward the *valley*. This forms a *shutter fold*.

3. Fold one of the inside edges of the shutter back to the outside fold. This fold forms a floppy "L."

4. Glue the floppy L-tab down to the base so that it forms a strong, straight L-tab.

5. Glue the other shutter side to the front of this L-tab. This forms a tent that is the backboard for the flashcards or student work to be displayed.

6. Fold the edge of the L-tab up one-quarter to one-half to form a lip that will keep the student work from slipping off the holder.

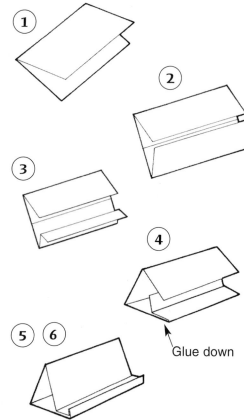

Glue down

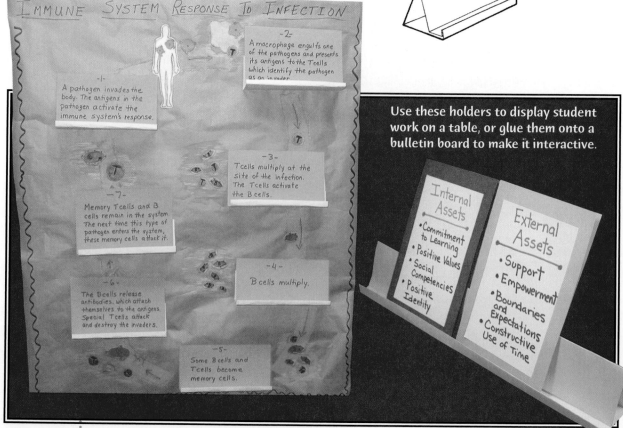

Use these holders to display student work on a table, or glue them onto a bulletin board to make it interactive.

Chapter Activities for
Glencoe Health

The pages that follow contain chapter-specific Foldables activities to use with *Glencoe Health*. Included are a Chapter Summary, a reproduction of the Foldables Study Organizer that appears on each chapter opener in the textbook, and a Follow-Up Foldables Activity. Use the Follow-Up Activity after students have studied each chapter. Students are asked to use the Foldables they have created and completed during the study of each chapter to review important chapter concepts and prepare for the chapter test.

Alternative Foldables activities are also included for every chapter. Use these activities during the study of each chapter or as chapter review activities. The Student Study Tip provides reading, writing, and test-taking strategies that you can share with your students throughout the course.

Living a Healthy Life

CHAPTER SUMMARY

Health is the combination of physical, mental/emotional, and social well-being. A person's health, at any moment, is a point along a continuum. People make choices each day that can affect their health positively or negatively. People who are health literate have the capacity to promote their own health and wellness. They keep the three elements of the health triangle—physical, mental/emotional, and social well-being—in balance. Influences on health include heredity, environment, attitude, behavior, media, and technology. Teens can take responsibility for their own health by understanding health risks and abstaining from risk behaviors.

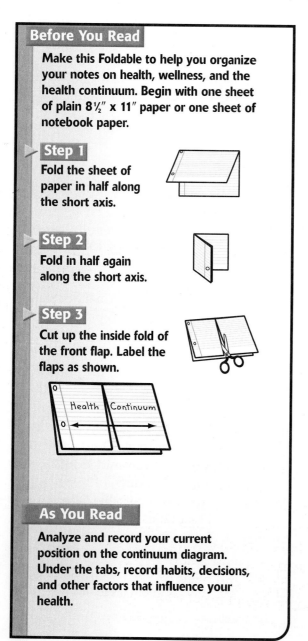

Before You Read

Make this Foldable to help you organize your notes on health, wellness, and the health continuum. Begin with one sheet of plain 8½" x 11" paper or one sheet of notebook paper.

Step 1

Fold the sheet of paper in half along the short axis.

Step 2

Fold in half again along the short axis.

Step 3

Cut up the inside fold of the front flap. Label the flaps as shown.

Health | Continuum

As You Read

Analyze and record your current position on the continuum diagram. Under the tabs, record habits, decisions, and other factors that influence your health.

CHAPTER REVIEW

Foldables Follow-Up Activity

Have the class set up its own "talk show" in which a moderator asks questions of the guests about their own experiences. Questions should focus on how responsibility, discipline, and positive direction can alter one's position on the health continuum. Suggest they refer to the information in their foldables.

TEACHER NOTES

_____
_____
_____
_____
_____
_____
_____
_____
_____
_____
_____
_____
_____

Alternative Activities for Chapter 1

COMPARING

Have students create a new foldable, label the tabs The Health Triangle and Influences on Health, and make notes under the tabs. Divide the class into small groups. Ask each group to research a particular year (or range of years) in American history, such as 1890, 1914, 1930, 1941, 1950, and 1965. Have them focus on the life of teens during that time and how adolescent health might have been affected by current influences. How do those influences compare to influences today? Would maintaining health have been easier or harder? Why? Ask each group to present its findings to the class.

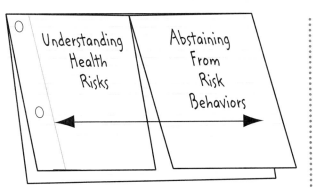

ROLE-PLAYING

Ask students to create a new foldable, label the tabs Understanding Health Risks and Abstaining from Risk Behaviors, and make notes or write examples under the tabs. Write on the chalkboard "Mature people are able to act in their own best interests." Ask teams of students to role-play situations to which this statement would apply.

Student Study Tip

Encourage students to get to know their textbooks so they can find things quickly and are not confused by assignments. Point out the different features, such as the Health Skills Activity and the Real-Life Application, and that every chapter has both lesson reviews and a chapter review. Show them how the Glossary lists chapter and page number where the terms can be found in context.

Building Health Skills and Character

CHAPTER SUMMARY

Health skills are tools and strategies that help people maintain, protect, and improve health. They include interpersonal skills, self-management skills, the ability to analyze influences, the ability to access information, and advocacy. Decision-making skills are steps that help people make healthful decisions. Setting both short-and long-term goals helps people build self-confidence, increase self-esteem, and improve overall health. Character is an outward expression of inner values.

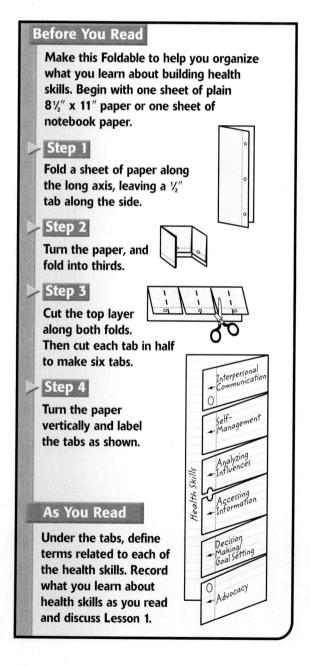

Before You Read

Make this Foldable to help you organize what you learn about building health skills. Begin with one sheet of plain 8½″ x 11″ paper or one sheet of notebook paper.

Step 1

Fold a sheet of paper along the long axis, leaving a ½″ tab along the side.

Step 2

Turn the paper, and fold into thirds.

Step 3

Cut the top layer along both folds. Then cut each tab in half to make six tabs.

Step 4

Turn the paper vertically and label the tabs as shown.

As You Read

Under the tabs, define terms related to each of the health skills. Record what you learn about health skills as you read and discuss Lesson 1.

CHAPTER REVIEW

Foldables Follow-Up Activity

Find photographs of adults whose clothing style is typical of an occupation or role. Include both positive and negative images. Cut out the photos or photocopy them to remove background context. Then ask students to identify the roles or occupations and the clues they used. Discuss with them how clothing, attitude, and certain behaviors send messages to others about whowe are and who we want to be.

TEACHER NOTES

_____
_____
_____
_____
_____
_____
_____
_____
_____
_____
_____
_____

Alternative Activities for Chapter 2

DESCRIBING

Have students create new foldables for the six steps in the decision-making process. Then have them use a separate sheet of paper and, referring to their foldables, describe a recent decision they've made and how they applied the six decision-making steps. If students can't think o a decision in which all six steps were used, ask them to describe a decision in which some "missing" steps might have helped.

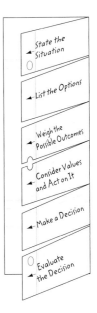

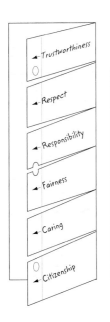

KEEPING A JOURNAL

Have students create a new foldable using the six traits of good character. When they've finished, ask them to keep a journal for at least a week. In their journal they should describe events each day in which at least one of the six traits played a part. At the end of the week, have volunteers read examples from their journals. Were students surprised by how many times character played a part in their activities? Why or why not?

Student Study Tip

Discuss with students how analyzing the results of a test or other assignment can often provide clues to doing better next time. Suggest that they ask themselves the following questions: Where did I do my best? Why? Was it because I knew the material well or because I find that type of question easier to answer? What was my biggest difficulty? Does any pattern appear? What caused my mistakes? Did I not follow directions or not study enough? Did I run out of time? How can I improve the results next time?

Chapter 2

FOLDABLES

Being a Health-Literate Consumer

CHAPTER SUMMARY

Informed health consumers are aware of the factors that influence their choices about health products and services. Health insurance helps most people pay for medical expenses. Some consumers have problems with health products, fraud, or malpractice. Several agencies are available to help people with these problems. Public health agencies administer health at both the local and national levels. Individuals can play a role in promoting public health.

Before You Read

Make this Foldable to help you organize what you learn about making consumer choices. Begin with one sheet of plain 8½" x 11" paper or one sheet of notebook paper.

Step 1

Fold a sheet of paper into thirds along the short axis.

Step 2

Unfold and label as shown.

Influences on Decisions	Your Rights as a Consumer	Today's Consumer Choices

As You Read

Under each label, take notes on what you learn about being a good consumer and making consumer choices.

CHAPTER REVIEW

Foldables Follow-Up Activity

Have students create an e-zine or Web page about adolescent health based on the information in their foldables and what they've learned so far in class. Suggest they make their publication entertaining and filled with interesting facts, warnings about fraudulent products, shopping tips, recipes, and hints for a healthier life. They might also wish to include links to other Web sites and an advice column to which other teens can write.

TEACHER NOTES

_____

_____

_____

_____

_____

_____

_____

_____

_____

_____

_____

Alternative Activities for Chapter 3

IDENTIFYING

Have students make new foldables in the form of a brochure about community health services. The brochure should list types of services, facilities, and trends in health care. Ask a health care professional to speak to the class about health-care trends, such as mind/body or holistic medicine. Ask students to prepare questions in advance.

Services	Facilities	Trends

Cost of Insurance	Cost of Services	Kinds of Malpractice

RESEARCHING

Have students create new foldables for keeping notes about the kinds of health fraud. Have students do research about malpractice. What is the cost of malpractice insurance for physicians? How much does it add to what the patient pays for services? What are some typical kinds of malpractice suits?

Student Study Tip

Suggest to students that they keep a homework and test planner similar to the ones adults use for their work. A planner should have space for noting the class, the date the assignment was made, the date it's due, important information about the assignment such as page numbers, and a list of any materials needed. At the end of the day, they can pull out the planner and know exactly what's expected of them and when they must turn assignments in.

Chapter 3

FOLDABLES

Physical Activity for Life

CHAPTER SUMMARY

Regular physical activity benefits physical, mental/emotional, and social health. Inactivity has many health risks. The five elements of fitness include cardio respiratory endurance, muscular strength, muscular endurance, flexibility, and body composition. Each element responds to different types of exercise. The best way to build fitness into daily routines is to set realistic physical activity goals. A basic program includes a warm-up, the workout, and a cool-down. Every training program should emphasize safety. Injuries include weather-related risks, minor injuries, and major injuries.

Before You Read

Make this Foldable to record what you learn about the benefits of physical activity and the risks of physical inactivity. Begin with one sheet of 11" x 17" paper.

Step 1

Fold the short sides of the paper inward so that they meet in the middle.

Step 2

Label as shown.

Benefits of Physical Activity | Risks of Physical Activity

As You Read

Under each label, take notes, define terms, record examples and draw your own conclusions about the importance of physical activity and the risks of physical inactivity.

CHAPTER REVIEW

Foldables Follow-Up Activity

Have students design and carry out a survey of both teens and adults to discover attitudes about physical activity and how people fit it into their lives. When they have finished, ask them to graph the information.

TEACHER NOTES

_____
_____
_____
_____
_____
_____
_____
_____
_____
_____
_____
_____
_____
_____
_____
_____

Alternative Activities for Chapter 4

ORGANIZING DATA

Have students create new foldables labeled Elements of Fitness and Improving Fitness. Have them measure strength, endurance, flexibility, and body composition as outlined in the text and record the information in the foldable behind the first fold. Behind the second fold, have them list goals for improved fitness and the steps they will take.

EVALUATING

Have students create new foldables labeled Training and Peak Performance and Safety First. Under the tabs have them take notes, define terms, and record examples. Ask volunteers to read books written by well-known coaches or trainers and evaluate the authors' methods for obtaining the best performances from athletes.

Student Study Tip

Suggest that students be sure they are familiar with everything the library has to offer and that they ask the librarian to bring them up to date on how to use any new resources. They should understand the way nonfiction books are organized according to call numbers and how to read the periodical indexes. If there is an electronic or online version of the indexes, they should be sure they know how to access it. They should also understand how to use the microform reader and how to obtain microfiche or microfilm files.

Nutrition and Your Health

CHAPTER SUMMARY

Good nutrition enhances quality of life and helps protect against disease. Hunger and appetite, emotions, and the environment all influence food choices. The six groups of nutrients include carbohydrates, proteins, fats, vitamins, minerals, and water. They are all needed for maximum energy and wellness. The *Dietary Guidelines for Americans* and the Food Guide Pyramid help people develop healthy eating habits. Reading food labels can help people make better food choices. Some people have food sensitivities. Everyone can reduce the risk of food borne illness by remembering these steps: clean, separate, cook, and chill.

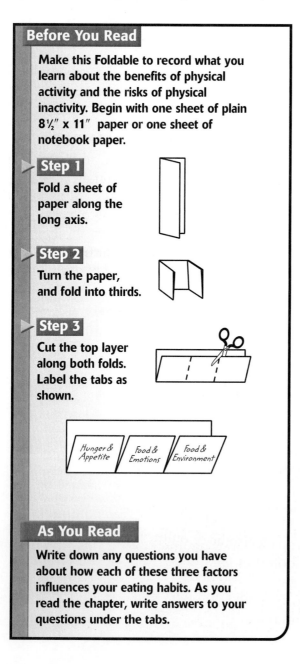

Before You Read

Make this Foldable to record what you learn about the benefits of physical activity and the risks of physical inactivity. Begin with one sheet of plain 8½" x 11" paper or one sheet of notebook paper.

▶ **Step 1**

Fold a sheet of paper along the long axis.

▶ **Step 2**

Turn the paper, and fold into thirds.

▶ **Step 3**

Cut the top layer along both folds. Label the tabs as shown.

Hunger & Appetite   Food & Emotions   Food & Environment

As You Read

Write down any questions you have about how each of these three factors influences your eating habits. As you read the chapter, write answers to your questions under the tabs.

CHAPTER REVIEW

Foldables Follow-Up Activity

Ask students to research and write a report on recent studies that show many young people in the U.S. are overweight. At the end of the report they should evaluate the information in terms of the people they observe in their own community. Ask students: Does the same percentage of people seem to be overweight? If so, what should be done?

TEACHER NOTES

_____

_____

_____

_____

_____

_____

_____

_____

_____

_____

_____

Alternative Activities for Chapter 5

ANALYZING

Have students create two new foldables, labeling one Carbohydrates, Proteins, and Fats and the other Vitamins, Minerals, and Water. Have them use the foldables to organize data about each type of nutrient. Ask groups of students to research foods eaten in the traditional diets of native peoples, such as the Navajo. How do the traditional foods compare nutritionally to today's convenience foods? What happens to the health of those who give up their traditional diets in favor of more modern, processed foods?

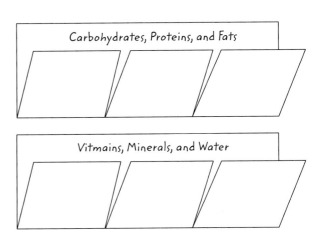

ORGANIZING

Have students create new foldables labeled Aim for Fitness, Build a Healthy Base, and Choose Sensibly and write notes and examples under the tabs. Work with the family and consumer sciences teacher to help students organize a school food fair that features ethnic foods and healthy food choices.

Student Study Tip

Remind students that they can't win at a game, such as tennis, if they're not on the court with the other players. They can't do well in school if they don't show up or don't pay attention in class. While they're skipping class or being inattentive, the game goes on without them. If they must miss class for legitimate reasons, such as a doctor's appointment, encourage them to obtain the assignments ahead of time. If that is not possible, encourage them to arrange to make up the work afterwards.

Managing Weight and Body Composition

CHAPTER SUMMARY

Weight is influenced by gender, age, height, body frame, growth rate, metabolic rate, and activity level. Being overweight or underweight involves health risks. Fad diets also involve health risks. Eating disorders are extreme, harmful eating behaviors leading to serious illness or even death. They require medical assistance. Dietary supplements may be appropriate for some people in order to meet nutrient needs. People have different nutritional needs at different stages of life.

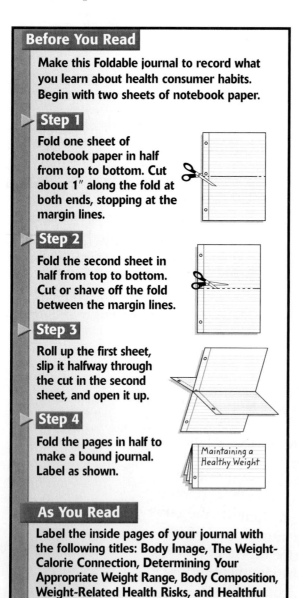

Before You Read

Make this Foldable journal to record what you learn about health consumer habits. Begin with two sheets of notebook paper.

Step 1

Fold one sheet of notebook paper in half from top to bottom. Cut about 1″ along the fold at both ends, stopping at the margin lines.

Step 2

Fold the second sheet in half from top to bottom. Cut or shave off the fold between the margin lines.

Step 3

Roll up the first sheet, slip it halfway through the cut in the second sheet, and open it up.

Step 4

Fold the pages in half to make a bound journal. Label as shown.

Maintaining a Healthy Weight

As You Read

Label the inside pages of your journal with the following titles: Body Image, The Weight-Calorie Connection, Determining Your Appropriate Weight Range, Body Composition, Weight-Related Health Risks, and Healthful Ways to Manage Weight. Use your journal to take notes as you read the chapter.

CHAPTER REVIEW

Foldables Follow-Up Activity

Ask students to obtain from the library a book or videotape on weight loss and evaluate the program based on the information in their foldables and what they've learned in this chapter.

TEACHER NOTES

_____

_____

_____

_____

_____

_____

_____

_____

_____

_____

_____

_____

_____

_____

_____

_____

_____

Alternative Activities for Chapter 6

IDENTIFYING

Have students create new foldables with the title Eating Disorders. Have them divide the booklet into three sections of two pages each and label the sections Anorexia Nervosa, Bulimia Nervosa, and Binge Eating. Have them use their foldables to take notes and write examples. Many teens think diet colas help them control weight. Direct them toward such resources as the Center for Science in the Public Interest to identify the ingredients in diet colas and any health risks or benefits involved.

EATING MINDFULLY

Have students create new foldables titled Nutrition for Individual Needs. They should label the inside pages Performance Nutrition, Vegetarianism, Dietary Supplements, Nutrition Throughout the Life Span, and Vocabulary. Have them make notes and define terms in the appropriate places. Discuss with the class the idea of eating "mindfully." This means bringing awareness as they eat to the sensations of taste and texture instead of thinking of other things and eating automatically. Suggest they try it to see if it helps prevent overeating.

Student Study Tip

Remind the class that instructors are as different from one another as teens are from other teens. For example, some teachers are relaxed; others are formal. It's part of a student's job to understand the teacher's expectations for such things as behavior and class participation. Suggest that students observe the teacher's style, listen carefully to instructions, and take notes. If that doesn't help, encourage them to arrange for a one-on-one session in which matters can be clarified. Remind them that teachers are their allies in building a successful life.

Chapter 6

FOLDABLES

Achieving Good Mental Health

CHAPTER SUMMARY

Good mental/emotional health is the ability to accept oneself and others, adapt to and manage emotions, and deal with life's demands and challenges. Maslow's hierarchy of needs organizes human needs in the form of a pyramid. Personality is an important factor in how a person meets those needs. Developmental assets help teens grow up as healthy, caring, and responsible individuals. Emotions are signals that tell the mind and body how to react.

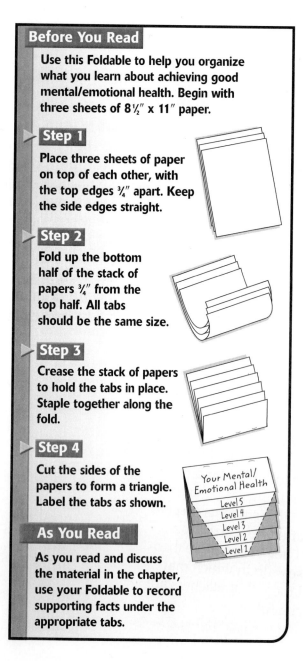

Before You Read

Use this Foldable to help you organize what you learn about achieving good mental/emotional health. Begin with three sheets of 8½" x 11" paper.

Step 1

Place three sheets of paper on top of each other, with the top edges ¾" apart. Keep the side edges straight.

Step 2

Fold up the bottom half of the stack of papers ¾" from the top half. All tabs should be the same size.

Step 3

Crease the stack of papers to hold the tabs in place. Staple together along the fold.

Step 4

Cut the sides of the papers to form a triangle. Label the tabs as shown.

Your Mental/
Emotional Health
Level 5
Level 4
Level 3
Level 2
Level 1

As You Read

As you read and discuss the material in the chapter, use your Foldable to record supporting facts under the appropriate tabs.

CHAPTER REVIEW

Foldables Follow-Up Activity

Discuss with students the various needs for volunteers in your community and how volunteering can contribute to feelings of self-worth. Have them research the wide range of opportunities from homeland security to child care. Guide them in assembling a database of this information that they can make available to the rest of the school or as a link in their e-zine.

TEACHER NOTES

_____
_____
_____
_____
_____
_____
_____
_____
_____
_____
_____
_____
_____

Alternative Activities for Chapter 7

EVALUATING

Have students create new foldables titled Your Personal Identity. Have them label the tabs Interests, Likes and Dislikes, Talents and Abilities, Values and Beliefs, and Goals. Then have them identify the different parts of the puzzle under the tabs. Ask students to obtain a popular self-help book on emotional health from the library and evaluate what it recommends in terms of what they're learning in class.

PROBLEM SOLVING

Have students create new foldables titled Managing Difficult Emotions. Have them label the tabs Defense Mechanisms, Handling Fear, Dealing with Guilt, Managing Anger, and Vocabulary and use the foldables to make notes and define terms. Discuss with students the value of meditation in managing difficult emotions and promoting health. Ask a health care professional to speak to the class on meditation.

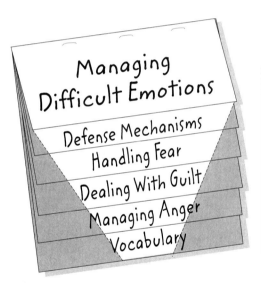

Student Study Tip

Suggest to students that they keep a record of their achievements in class and that they reward themselves when they succeed. A chart is useful for keeping track of grades and other achievements. But grades are only one aspect of success. Suggest that they note skills or topics they are struggling with and record goals met. You might let the class brainstorm possible rewards for meeting positive goals. Rewards do not have to be extravagant or cost money.

Chapter 7

FOLDABLES

Managing Stress and Anxiety
CHAPTER SUMMARY

Stress is a normal part of life; however, too much stress over too long a time can affect physical, mental/emotional, and social health. Identifying stressors and learning to manage stress can help people stay healthy and prevent disease. Stressors occurring during the teen years can cause anxiety and even depression. Teens with persistent anxiety or depression should seek professional help. Resilient people find it easier to adapt effectively and recover from disappointment, difficulty, or crisis.

Before You Read

Use this Foldable to help you organize what you learn about the causes and effects of stress. Begin with a sheet of 8½" x 11" paper.

Step 1
Fold the sheet of paper into thirds along the short axis.

Step 2
Unfold. Fold a long end of the sheet down to form a 1" tab.

Step 3
Unfold and label as shown.

Stress	Cause	Effect

As You Read

As you read and discuss the material in the chapter, use your Foldable to record examples of stress you experience, to analyze the cause of the stress, and to note the effects of the stress on your life.

CHAPTER REVIEW

Foldables Follow-Up Activity

Ask students to recall a recent stressful experience and, on a separate sheet of paper, write a short story about someone having a similar experience and how that person is able to take control.

TEACHER NOTES

_____

_____

_____

_____

_____

_____

_____

_____

_____

_____

_____

_____

_____

_____

_____

_____

_____

_____

_____

_____

Alternative Activities for Chapter 8

SHARING EXPERIENCES

Have students make new foldables and label the columns Experiences with Anxiety, How I Managed, and Finding Help, and create a chart of their own experiences with anxiety. Ask volunteers to locate Internet chat rooms devoted to managing anxiety and depression. Preview the sites yourself for appropriateness, then have interested students participate and share their experiences with the class.

Experiences with Anxiety	How I Managed	Finding Help

ANALYZING

Have students create new foldables to organize data on resiliency. Have them label the columns External Resiliency Factors, Internal Resiliency Factors, and Protective Factors and use the chart to record examples. Write on the chalkboard the following statement based on a quotation from Thomas A. Edison: "I have not failed 10,000 times. I have successfully found 10,000 ways that will not work." Discuss with the class what this quote reveals about Edison's resiliency based on what they have learned in class. Have them describe ways in which they might apply his attitude to their own experience.

External Resiliency Factors	Internal Resiliency Factors	Protective Factors

Student Study Tip

Ask a volunteer to define the word *procrastination*. Discuss how it means putting off doing what needs to be done and how it can lead to anxiety. Procrastination can be a tough habit to break. One of the first steps in doing so is to recognize that the problem exists. Suggest to students that they prioritize their tasks. Which tasks are urgent and need to be handled right away? Which can be done the next day? Caution them to be honest in their evaluation. Then encourage them to schedule the tasks in order of priority.

Chapter 8

FOLDABLES

Mental and Emotional Problems

CHAPTER SUMMARY

Mental disorders include anxiety disorders, mood disorders, eating disorders, conduct disorders, schizophrenia, and personality disorders. Recognizing the warning signs of suicide can help in suicide prevention. Symptoms of mental disorders include prolonged sadness for no apparent reason, frequent outbursts of anger, overwhelming fear, anxiety, or anger at the world, unexplainable changes in sleeping or eating habits, and social withdrawal.

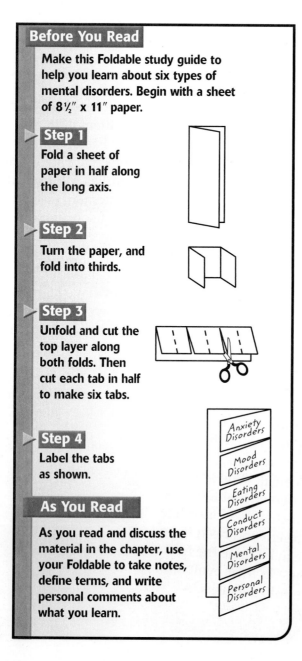

Before You Read

Make this Foldable study guide to help you learn about six types of mental disorders. Begin with a sheet of 8½" x 11" paper.

Step 1

Fold a sheet of paper in half along the long axis.

Step 2

Turn the paper, and fold into thirds.

Step 3

Unfold and cut the top layer along both folds. Then cut each tab in half to make six tabs.

Step 4

Label the tabs as shown.

Anxiety Disorders
Mood Disorders
Eating Disorders
Conduct Disorders
Mental Disorders
Personal Disorders

As You Read

As you read and discuss the material in the chapter, use your Foldable to take notes, define terms, and write personal comments about what you learn.

CHAPTER REVIEW

Foldables Follow-Up Activity

Discuss with students how, until the late nineteenth century, people with even mild mental and emotional disorders were often locked away in the family home or in large institutions along with criminals. Mental illness carried a severe social stigma for the families. Is there still a stigma today? If so, in what ways?

TEACHER NOTES

_____

_____

_____

_____

_____

_____

_____

_____

_____

_____

_____

_____

_____

Alternative Activities for Chapter 9

RESEARCHING

Have students create new foldables and label the tabs with the six different types of mental health professionals. Have students research work done by pioneers in mental health, such as Freud, Jung, and Adler, and write a short paper on their methods and important theories.

INCREASING AWARENESS

Have students create new foldables, writing the title Therapy Methods on the top tab and the names of the five methods on the remaining tabs. Have them take notes and define the methods under the tabs. Ask a mental health professional or the school counselor to talk with the class about mental and emotional problems that often affect teens and ways to get help. Ask the class to prepare questions for the speaker in advance.

Student Study Tip

Some students become anxious about taking tests. Adequate preparation can help prevent anxiety. Suggest that they ask teachers what material will be covered on the test and what type of questions will be used. Essay questions may require broader understanding and fewer factual details than objective questions. Suggest they study over several days and then merely review on the final day rather than cramming. They should get enough sleep the night before, exercise to relieve tension, eat a good breakfast, and maintain a positive attitude.

Chapter 9

FOLDABLES

Skills for Healthy Relationships

CHAPTER SUMMARY

All of a person's relationships have an effect on physical, mental/emotional, and social health. Communication, cooperation, and compromise form the basis for healthy relationships. Basic communication skills include speaking, listening, and body language. People can develop more effective communication skills. Conflicts are a normal part of life. Conflict resolution can result when people show respect for themselves and others, are willing to negotiate, and agree to mediation.

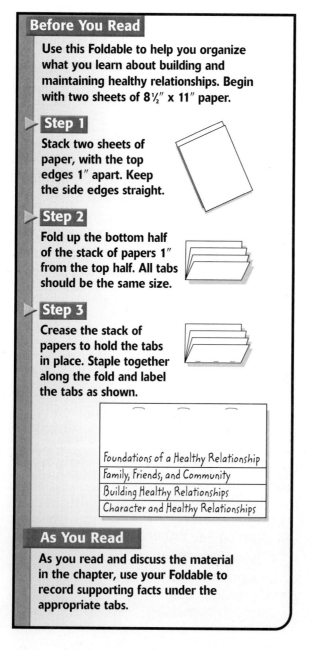

Before You Read

Use this Foldable to help you organize what you learn about building and maintaining healthy relationships. Begin with two sheets of 8½" x 11" paper.

Step 1

Stack two sheets of paper, with the top edges 1" apart. Keep the side edges straight.

Step 2

Fold up the bottom half of the stack of papers 1" from the top half. All tabs should be the same size.

Step 3

Crease the stack of papers to hold the tabs in place. Staple together along the fold and label the tabs as shown.

Foundations of a Healthy Relationship
Family, Friends, and Community
Building Healthy Relationships
Character and Healthy Relationships

As You Read

As you read and discuss the material in the chapter, use your Foldable to record supporting facts under the appropriate tabs.

CHAPTER REVIEW

Foldables Follow-Up Activity

Tape an older TV situation comedy that uses positive humor, such as *The Dick Van Dyke Show* or *The Andy Griffith Show*, and show it to the class. Ask them to compare it to more current comedies that depend heavily on insults and humiliation for laughs. Ask students to write a paragraph describing the meaning of friendship as it is displayed in each show. Which characters would they rather have as friends, and which would they want around in times of trouble?

TEACHER NOTES

_____

_____

_____

_____

_____

_____

_____

_____

_____

Alternative Activities for Chapter 10

BRAINSTORMING

Have students create new foldables and label the tabs Communication Styles, Speaking Skills, Listening Skills, and Nonverbal Communication. Have them write the relevant main ideas under each tab. Discuss with students how we have all been disappointed when someone isn't straight with us, as though the person isn't comfortable with telling us the truth. Divide the class into groups for brainstorming reasons why a person might do this and how to recognize telltale signs in the person's behavior. What might the person really be trying to tell us?

| Communication Styles |
| Speaking Skills |
| Listening Skills |
| Nonverbal Communication |

ANALYZING

Have students make new foldables and title them Conflict Resolution. Then have them write Respect for Oneself and Others, Negotiating, and Mediation on the tabs. Have them write notes and examples under the tabs. Encourage students to prepare and produce a program on conflict resolution for the local community access TV channel. They might hold a round-table or panel discussion or conduct interviews of other teens.

| Conflict Resolution |
| Respect for Oneself and Others |
| Negotiating |
| Mediation |

Student Study Tip

Discuss with students how studying in groups can have both advantages and disadvantages. Members can take turns quizzing one another on the material or helping one another understand puzzling information. Members can exchange notes made in class to get a more rounded view of the subject. However, groups can be distracting and big time-wasters. More time can be spent socializing than studying. Suggest that students evaluate group studying carefully based on how productive it is for them in each circumstance.

Chapter 10

FOLDABLES

Family Relationships

CHAPTER SUMMARY

The family is the basic unit of society and provides a safe and nurturing environment for its members. It is possible to strengthen family relationships. Family structures can change as a result of separation or divorce, remarriage, or the death of a family member. It is important to learn to manage the stress caused by these changes. Family crises can sometimes lead to violence. Using the three Rs—recognize, resist, and report—can help people prevent violence. Communities offer professional health services to families facing crises. In addition, each family member can do his or her part in keeping the family healthy.

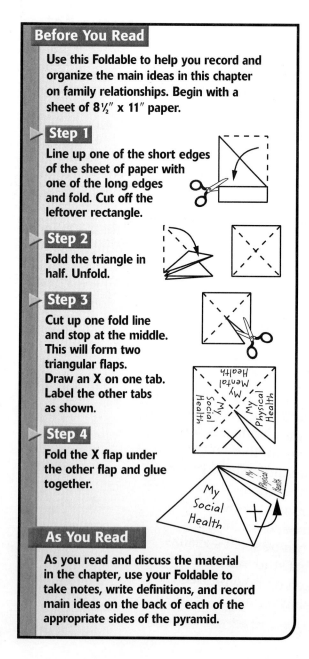

Before You Read

Use this Foldable to help you record and organize the main ideas in this chapter on family relationships. Begin with a sheet of 8½″ x 11″ paper.

Step 1

Line up one of the short edges of the sheet of paper with one of the long edges and fold. Cut off the leftover rectangle.

Step 2

Fold the triangle in half. Unfold.

Step 3

Cut up one fold line and stop at the middle. This will form two triangular flaps. Draw an X on one tab. Label the other tabs as shown.

Step 4

Fold the X flap under the other flap and glue together.

As You Read

As you read and discuss the material in the chapter, use your Foldable to take notes, write definitions, and record main ideas on the back of each of the appropriate sides of the pyramid.

CHAPTER REVIEW

Foldables Follow-Up Activity

Make students aware of Web sites for families in which they can create their own free, private, Web page for helping family members stay connected. They can upload photos, post news, and develop a family tree. Some sites also offer information on topics of interest to families.

TEACHER NOTES

Alternative Activities for Chapter 11

COMPOSING

Have students create new foldables and label the sides Separation and Divorce, Remarriage, and Death of a Family Member. Have them record main ideas in the space provided. Discuss with the class how older people can often be critical of the way the "younger generation" lives. Ask students to compare this reaction with how they might sometimes feel with a younger sibling. Have them compose a story or essay about how older people can be important repositories of information about life and the values that sustain families.

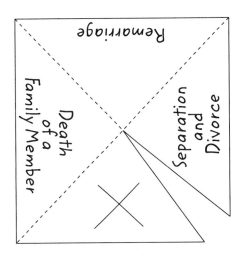

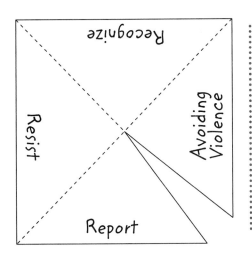

SHARING INFORMATION

Have students create new foldables and label the peak Avoiding Violence and the sides Recognize, Resist, and Report. Have them record main ideas in the space provided. Discuss with students how crises often affect a family's dreams for the future. Ask students to identify dreams their parents have had for the family. Ask them to share their own dreams. What kind of future do they imagine for their own children? How will they protect those dreams?

Student Study Tip

Ask students if they have a special place to study at home. If not, suggest they find one and shape it to their needs. A study spot should be comfortable, have a smooth surface for writing and for spreading papers out, have good lighting, be free of clutter, and be reasonably peaceful and quiet. These features aid concentration and make it easier to stay organized. They should also be sure to keep enough supplies on hand nearby, as well as a wastebasket and resources, such as a dictionary.

Chapter 11

FOLDABLES

Peer Relationships

CHAPTER SUMMARY

Peer relationships include friendships and cliques. Building healthy friendships is important during the teen years. Peer pressure can have a positive or negative influence on a person's behavior. Teens can develop skills for resisting negative peer pressure. Dating can be an enjoyable learning experience. To avoid risk situations, wise teens learn to set limits. Abstinence from sexual activity is the only sure way to prevent pregnancy and sexually transmitted diseases. Teens can say no by using avoidance techniques and refusal skills.

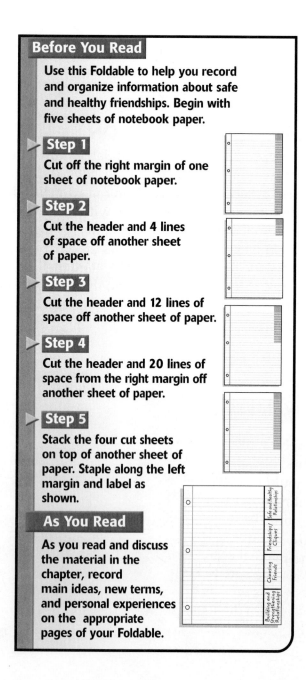

Before You Read

Use this Foldable to help you record and organize information about safe and healthy friendships. Begin with five sheets of notebook paper.

Step 1

Cut off the right margin of one sheet of notebook paper.

Step 2

Cut the header and 4 lines of space off another sheet of paper.

Step 3

Cut the header and 12 lines of space off another sheet of paper.

Step 4

Cut the header and 20 lines of space from the right margin off another sheet of paper.

Step 5

Stack the four cut sheets on top of another sheet of paper. Staple along the left margin and label as shown.

As You Read

As you read and discuss the material in the chapter, record main ideas, new terms, and personal experiences on the appropriate pages of your Foldable.

CHAPTER REVIEW

Foldables Follow-Up Activity

Work with teachers at other schools to establish a telecollaborative project in which students are paired up as e-mail pen pals to exchange information and experiences regarding health issues and peer relationships. Remind students to use proper etiquette (e-mail and chat room etiquette) when corresponding online.

TEACHER NOTES

_____
_____
_____
_____
_____
_____
_____
_____
_____
_____
_____
_____
_____
_____

Alternative Activities for Chapter 12

PROBLEM SOLVING

Have students make new foldables titled Peer Pressure and Refusal Skills. Have them label the tabs with topics from the lesson and make notes and define terms on the appropriate pages. Divide the class into small groups to discuss ways in which a person's self-concept and self-esteem can help the person cope with peer pressure.

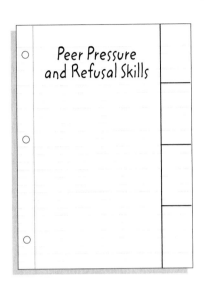

SYNTHESIZING

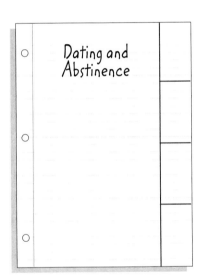

Have students make new foldables titled Dating and Abstinence. Have them label the tabs with topics from the lessons and make notes and define terms on the appropriate pages. Divide the class into small groups. Ask each group to create a photo essay or multimedia presentation titled Dating Challenges. Encourage them to have fun with it and be creative.

Student Study Tip

Although most students will have some experience researching information in an encyclopedia, they may rely too heavily on paging through volumes organized alphabetically. Point out that the full range of information about a particular topic is listed in the index. The index also makes searching under related topics easier. Students accustomed to using electronic encyclopedias should check both the browse and search functions. Remind them that almost all encyclopedias publish a yearbook that contains the most up-to-date information available at the time of printing. Some encyclopedias publish this data online.

Chapter 12

FOLDABLES

Violence Prevention

CHAPTER SUMMARY

Strategies for staying safe include taking precautions, using body language and self-defense, and following tips to keep the home safe. Residents can contribute to community safety. Issues of school safety include bullying, sexual harassment, and gangs. Recognizing warning signs can reduce the risk of violence. Influences on violence include the media, alcohol and other drugs, and mental/emotional issues. Assault, homicide, and sexual violence are the violent crimes for which teens are most often arrested. Abuse of one person by another may be physical, mental/emotional, or sexual. Victims of abuse should seek counseling.

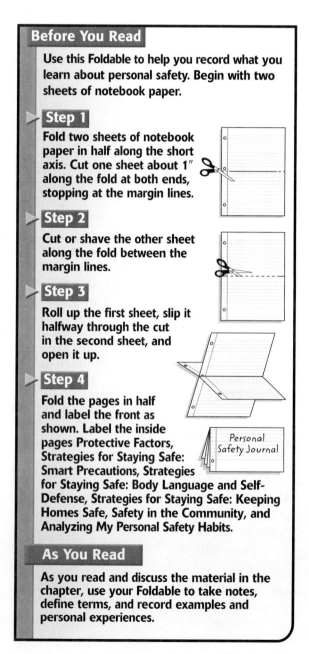

Before You Read

Use this Foldable to help you record what you learn about personal safety. Begin with two sheets of notebook paper.

Step 1

Fold two sheets of notebook paper in half along the short axis. Cut one sheet about 1" along the fold at both ends, stopping at the margin lines.

Step 2

Cut or shave the other sheet along the fold between the margin lines.

Step 3

Roll up the first sheet, slip it halfway through the cut in the second sheet, and open it up.

Step 4

Fold the pages in half and label the front as shown. Label the inside pages Protective Factors, Strategies for Staying Safe: Smart Precautions, Strategies for Staying Safe: Body Language and Self-Defense, Strategies for Staying Safe: Keeping Homes Safe, Safety in the Community, and Analyzing My Personal Safety Habits.

Personal Safety Journal

As You Read

As you read and discuss the material in the chapter, use your Foldable to take notes, define terms, and record examples and personal experiences.

CHAPTER REVIEW

Foldables Follow-Up Activity

Because of all the emphasis on violence in the media, teens can sometimes feel overwhelmed and fearful. Suggest that they set aside at least one day a week for a news "fast", in which they do not watch the news on TV or read about violence in the newspapers.

TEACHER NOTES

_____

_____

_____

_____

_____

_____

_____

_____

_____

_____

_____

_____

_____

_____

_____

_____

_____

Alternative Activities for Chapter 13

ANALYZING

Have students create new foldables titled Peer Mediation. Have them label five inside pages with the steps in mediation and the sixth page What Our School Is Doing. Have them use the foldables to record main ideas. Discuss with the class how we are all heroes of our own life stories. People on both sides of a conflict see themselves as heroes defending their position. Ask students to write a short story from the points of view of people on both sides of a particular conflict.

DRAWING INFERENCES

Have students create new foldables titled Types of Violence and label inside pages Assault, Random Violence, Homicide, Sexual Assault, Rape, and Gang-Related Violence. Have them use the foldables to make notes and define terms. Discuss with students how conflict in books and movies is often positive. It creates interest. People want to know what's going to happen next. Does a sense of excitement accompany real-life conflict? What effect does this have on whether or not people want to take part in events like hazing or gang behavior?

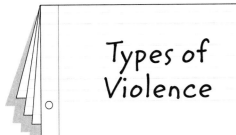

Student Study Tip

Remind students of the value of listing, grouping, and labeling. By categorizing terms or subjects in meaningful ways, they can understand how the items are related and organize their knowledge more effectively. Doing so also aids memory. Suggest that students try this strategy before a quiz or test to see if they retain the information better.

Personal Care and Healthy Behaviors

CHAPTER SUMMARY

The skin consists of two main layers and is the first line of defense against pathogens. Proper care keeps skin, hair, and nails healthy. Teeth and gums are important to health and appearance. They require regular brushing, flossing, and dental screenings. The function of the eye is to gather light. A healthy diet, eye protection, and regular vision screenings all contribute to eye health. Ears are responsible for balance as well as hearing. Proper ear care includes protection from injury and loud noises.

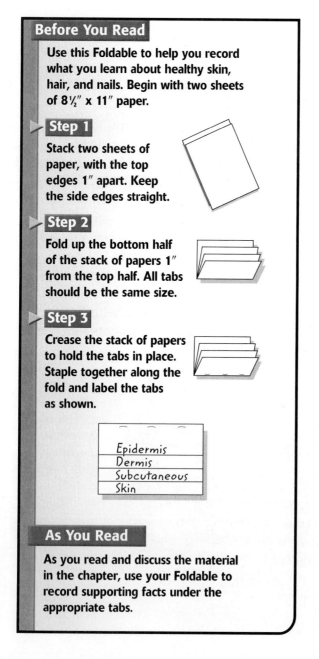

Before You Read

Use this Foldable to help you record what you learn about healthy skin, hair, and nails. Begin with two sheets of 8½" x 11" paper.

Step 1

Stack two sheets of paper, with the top edges 1" apart. Keep the side edges straight.

Step 2

Fold up the bottom half of the stack of papers 1" from the top half. All tabs should be the same size.

Step 3

Crease the stack of papers to hold the tabs in place. Staple together along the fold and label the tabs as shown.

Epidermis
Dermis
Subcutaneous
Skin

As You Read

As you read and discuss the material in the chapter, use your Foldable to record supporting facts under the appropriate tabs.

CHAPTER REVIEW

Foldables Follow-Up Activity

In recent years several books have been written about brand-name cosmetics, questioning the advertising used and their value as consumer products. Ask volunteers to read at least one of the books and report to the class on their findings.

TEACHER NOTES

_____
_____
_____
_____
_____
_____
_____
_____
_____
_____
_____
_____
_____
_____

Alternative Activities for Chapter 14

RESEARCHING

Have students create new foldables titled Eyes and label the tabs Parts of the Eye, Vision Problems, and Diseases of the Eye. Have them use the foldables to record main ideas. Students may be interested in learning more about current research in computer implants that can restore at least partial sight to people who have lost their vision. Some implants go directly into the eye; others are implanted into the brain. Ask volunteers to do research and share their findings.

Eyes
Parts of the Eye
Vision Problems
Diseases of the Eye

Ears
Parts of the Ear
Hearing and Balance
Problems of the Ear

DRAWING INFERENCES

Have students make new foldables titled Ears and label the tabs Parts of the Ear, Hearing and Balance, and Problems of the Ear. Discuss with students how sound is measured in decibels (dB) and inform them that nothing in nature, except volcanoes and violent thunder, is louder than 100 dB. Then ask them to graph these decibel measurements: quiet room 40; normal conversation 60; rush hour traffic 92; jackhammer 105; rock 'n roll band, near loudspeaker 110; chain saw 125; jet airplane engine, 100 feet away 140. What inferences can they draw?

Student Study Tip

A thesaurus can help students understand unfamiliar words and improve their report writing. If students are not familiar with a thesaurus, point out that it is a collection of synonyms and antonyms. If they are stuck for the right word or want to avoid repeating the same word, a thesaurus can provide the answer. Some volumes are organized alphabetically, others by category. Show them how to use the index to find what they're looking for. Point out that the numbers may not be page numbers but entry numbers. Point out that electronic versions may not offer as many choices.

Chapter 14

FOLDABLES

Skeletal, Muscular, and Nervous Systems

CHAPTER SUMMARY

The skeletal system consists of bones, cartilage, and joints. Problems of the skeletal system include fractures, osteoporosis, scoliosis, injuries to joints, and repetitive motion injuries. Smooth skeletal and cardiac muscles are part of the muscular system. Problems of the nervous system include head and spinal cord injuries, degenerative diseases, and other disorders.

Before You Read

Use this Foldable to help you organize your notes on the structure and function of the skeletal system, muscular system, and nervous system. Begin with three sheets of 8½" x 11" paper.

▶ **Step 1**

Fold the sheets of paper along the long axis so that one edge is about 1" from the other.

▶ **Step 2**

Fold the paper in half. Unfold and cut along the inside fold line.

▶ **Step 3**

Repeat with the other two sheets of paper. Label as shown. Staple the sheets together.

Muscular System
Structure | Function

Skeletal System
Structure | Function

Nervous System
Structure | Function

As You Read

As you read and discuss the material in the chapter, use your Foldable to record what you learn.

CHAPTER REVIEW

Foldables Follow-Up Activity

Gravity is essential to bone health, this is why weight-bearing exercise is emphasized for maintaining healthy bones. Discuss with students how astronauts on the International Space Station maintain healthy skeletal systems in spite of the low-gravity environment. Have them access NASA's Web site for information.

TEACHER NOTES

_____
_____
_____
_____
_____
_____
_____
_____
_____
_____
_____
_____
_____
_____
_____

Alternative Activities for Chapter 15

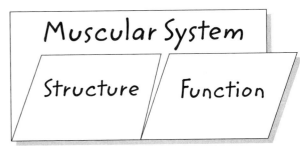

PROBLEM SOLVING

Have students create new foldables titled Muscular System and label the tabs Structure and Function. Have them make notes and define terms under the tabs. Divide the class into groups and have each group develop a series of exercises designed to work a particular set of muscles so that, when the exercises from all groups are combined, the class will have produced a total body workout.

INVESTIGATING

Have students make new foldables titled Nervous System, label the tabs Structure and Function, and make notes and define terms under the tabs. Develop with the class a study on multi-tasking and its effects on the nervous system. Are people being affected negatively or not? For example, you might have students design an experiment to establish the limits of a person's ability to multi-task, or students might research related topics and draw inferences, such as car accidents being caused by people who are eating or telephoning while driving.

Student Study Tip

Review with students how prefixes and suffixes contribute to the meaning of words. Prefixes are added to the beginning of a word and suffixes are added to the end. Write examples of prefixes and suffixes on the chalkboard, such as: de-, pre-, con-, inter-, -ive, and -tion. Have students look up a word from Chapter 15 and analyze its prefix, root word, and suffix.

Cardiovascular and Respiratory Systems
CHAPTER SUMMARY

The cardiovascular system includes the heart and all the blood vessels. Problems include congenital heart defects, cardiovascular disease, heart murmur, varicose veins, anemia, leukemia, and hemophilia. The respiratory system takes in oxygen and gives off carbon dioxide. It includes the lungs, other respiratory structures, the larynx, and the epiglottis. Respiratory system problems include bronchitis, pneumonia, asthma, sinusitis, tuberculosis, and emphysema.

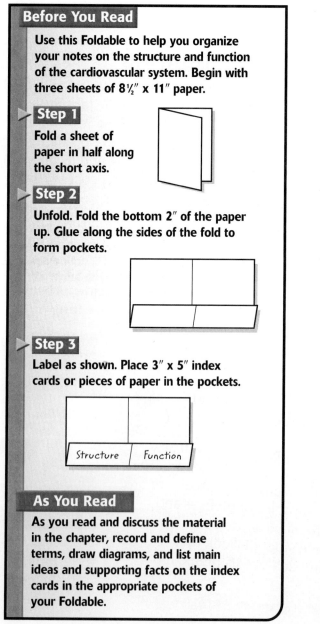

Before You Read

Use this Foldable to help you organize your notes on the structure and function of the cardiovascular system. Begin with three sheets of 8½" x 11" paper.

Step 1

Fold a sheet of paper in half along the short axis.

Step 2

Unfold. Fold the bottom 2" of the paper up. Glue along the sides of the fold to form pockets.

Step 3

Label as shown. Place 3" x 5" index cards or pieces of paper in the pockets.

Structure | Function

As You Read

As you read and discuss the material in the chapter, record and define terms, draw diagrams, and list main ideas and supporting facts on the index cards in the appropriate pockets of your Foldable.

CHAPTER REVIEW

Foldables Follow-Up Activity

Students may gain a better appreciation of the heart and its intricate relationship to the rest of the body by doing some research on artificial hearts. They may be surprised by the number of components and fail-safe mechanisms that are required. The AbioCor replacement heart is the latest version. Drawings and other information can be found online.

TEACHER NOTES

Alternative Activities for Chapter 16

REINFORCING CONCEPTS

Have students make new foldables for the cardiovascular system, label the pockets Problems and Care, and use them to organize their study cards. Invite a health care professional to demonstrate a stress test to the class and explain what the test reveals. Have students prepare questions for the speaker in advance based on what they've learned in class. Discuss with students the work of doctors like Dean Ornish who revolutionized thinking about heart disease by proving it could be reversed with lifestyle changes.

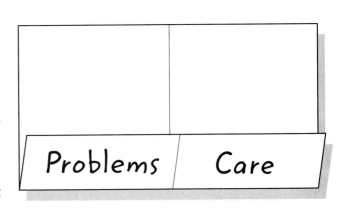

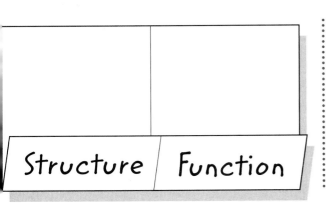

GRAPHING DATA

Have students create new foldables for the respiratory system, label the pockets Structure and Function, and use them to organize their study cards. Cases of asthma are on the increase in the U.S. Have students research relevant data on numbers of cases and graph the increase. Ask them to find out what experts think is the cause.

Student Study Tip

Remind students that mapping and outlining are two helpful ways of organizing notes and other material. For mapping, divide the paper into sections and jot down related words or phrases in the proper area. Mapping is more relaxed and its structure is looser. It is useful for creative thinking and making notes during brainstorming. Outlining is more precise and well suited to formal reports. The outline begins with a major idea. Major points about the topic follow. Sub-points and supporting details back up the major points. Provide examples for students on the chalkboard.

Chapter 16

FOLDABLES

Digestive and Urinary Systems
CHAPTER SUMMARY

Functions of the digestive system are digestion, absorption, and elimination. Structures include the esophagus, the stomach; the pancreas, liver, and gallbladder; the small intestine; and the large intestine. Digestion includes both mechanical and chemical changes. Problems of the digestive system may be functional or structural. The urinary system consists of the kidneys, the ureters, the bladder, and the urethra. It is responsible for removing water-soluble wastes from the body.

Before You Read

Make this Foldable to help you organize your notes on the structure and function of the digestive system. Begin with one sheet of plain 11″ x 17″ paper.

Step 1

Mark the midpoint of the long axis on a sheet of paper.

Step 2

Fold the outside edges of the paper in to touch the middle mark. Label as shown.

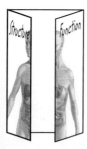

As You Read

As you read and discuss the material in the chapter, record what you learn about the structure and function of the digestive system under the appropriate side of your Foldable.

CHAPTER REVIEW

Foldables Follow-Up Activity

Discuss with students the technique of stomach stapling performed on certain people who are severely overweight. Ask volunteers to learn more about the process and any side effects and report their findings to the class.

TEACHER NOTES

_____

_____

_____

_____

_____

_____

_____

_____

_____

_____

_____

_____

_____

_____

_____

_____

Alternative Activities for Chapter 17

SHARING INFORMATION

Have students create new foldables for the digestive system, label the tabs Care and Problems, and use them to record main ideas. If students are publishing a newsletter or e-zine, have them include consumer information on over-the-counter medicines for digestive problems.

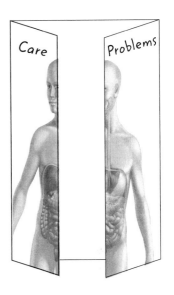

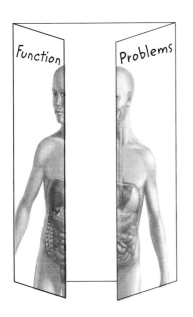

MONITORING

Have students create new foldables for the urinary system, label the tabs Function and Problems, and use them to record main ideas. Have students monitor their water (and other acceptable liquid) intake for one 24-hour period using a measuring cup and keeping a record. By how much must they increase their intake to meet the eight-cup goal?

Student Study Tip

Students are often asked to write reports based on research. Review with them the basics of citing sources. For magazines or newspapers, they must be sure to include the publication's name, date of the edition, title of the article, the writer's name, and the page number. For books they must include the title, author's name, copyright date, and page numbers for any specific citations. If they plan to use quoted material, they should be sure to copy it accurately and put quote marks around it.

Chapter 17 FOLDABLES

Endocrine and Reproductive Systems
CHAPTER SUMMARY

The endocrine system produces hormones that help regulate body functions and consists of the pituitary gland and the adrenal gland. The male reproductive system includes both internal and external organs. It produces and stores sperm and transfers sperm to the female's body. The female reproductive system includes several organs and glands. It produces female sex hormones, stores female reproductive cells, and nourishes and protects the fertilized ovum until birth.

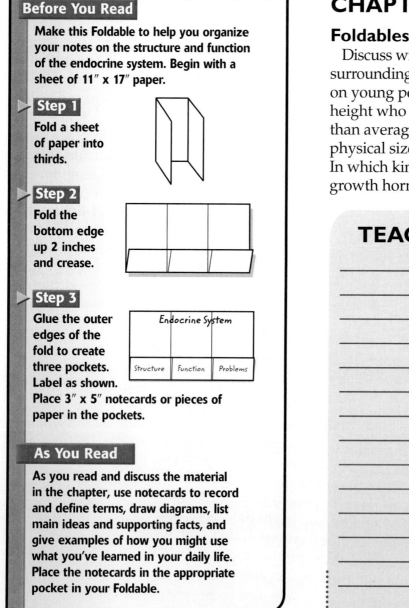

Before You Read

Make this Foldable to help you organize your notes on the structure and function of the endocrine system. Begin with a sheet of 11″ x 17″ paper.

Step 1

Fold a sheet of paper into thirds.

Step 2

Fold the bottom edge up 2 inches and crease.

Step 3

Glue the outer edges of the fold to create three pockets. Label as shown. Place 3″ x 5″ notecards or pieces of paper in the pockets.

Endocrine System

Structure | Function | Problems

As You Read

As you read and discuss the material in the chapter, use notecards to record and define terms, draw diagrams, list main ideas and supporting facts, and give examples of how you might use what you've learned in your daily life. Place the notecards in the appropriate pocket in your Foldable.

CHAPTER REVIEW

Foldables Follow-Up Activity

Discuss with students the controversy surrounding the use of growth hormone on young people who are of normal height who are simply a little shorter than average. What importance should physical size have to a person's worth? In which kinds of circumstances should growth hormone be used?

TEACHER NOTES

_____
_____
_____
_____
_____
_____
_____
_____
_____
_____
_____
_____
_____

Alternative Activities for Chapter 18

ANALYZING INFLUENCES

Have students make new foldables titled Male Reproductive System and label the pockets Structure, Function, and Problems Use the foldable to store notes, drawings, and definitions. Discuss with the class gender roles in different cultures. What influences these differences?

Male Reproductive System		
Structure	Function	Problems

Female Reproductive System		
Structure	Function	Problems

RESEARCHING

Have students make new foldables titled Female Reproductive System and label the pockets Structure, Function, and Problems Use the foldable to store notes, drawings, and definitions. Ask students to imagine they have received a letter from a younger teen who is entering puberty and is concerned about body changes. Ask them to write a letter to the person giving advice based on information learned in class.

Student Study Tip

Help students to make the best use of Internet resources by showing them how to evaluate a Web site. Suggest they create a Web site evaluation form featuring the following questions and that they refer to it when online: 1) Who owns the Web site? 2) What is the author's expertise? Are any credentials given? 3) Is the site's purpose to entertain, educate, sell, or persuade? 4) When was the information last updated? 5) Does the information seem biased? What makes you think so? 6) Is it well written, grammatically correct, and free of spelling errors, math errors, or other incorrect information?

Chapter 18

FOLDABLES

Prenatal Development and Birth

CHAPTER SUMMARY

Human development begins as the joining of a sperm cell and an egg cell. This zygote develops into an embryo and then a fetus. Stages of birth include dilation, passage through the birth canal, and afterbirth. Proper nutrition and care are essential during pregnancy. Alcohol, tobacco, and the misuse of medicines and drugs endanger the health of the fetus. The passing of traits from parents to children is called heredity. Genes are the basic units of heredity.

Before You Read

Make this Foldable to help you organize information on the beginning of life. Begin with a sheet of plain 8½" x 11" paper.

Step 1

Fold a sheet of paper along the long axis, leaving a ½" tab along the bottom.

Step 2

Fold in half, then fold again into fourths.

Step 3

Unfold and cut along the three fold lines on the front flap. Label as shown.

| Conception & Implantation | Embryonic Growth | Fetal Development | Labor |

The Beginning of the Life Cycle

As You Read

As you read and discuss the material in the chapter, use your Foldable to take notes, define terms, sketch diagrams, and explain the early stages of the life cycle.

CHAPTER REVIEW

Foldables Follow-Up Activity

The use of three-dimensional ultrasound images should be common within the next few years. Students may be interested in doing an Internet search to view an animated version of the technology, such as at *Technology Review's* Web site. Ask students to brainstorm other possible uses for 3-D ultrasound.

TEACHER NOTES

_____
_____
_____
_____
_____
_____
_____
_____
_____
_____
_____
_____

Alternative Activities for Chapter 19

RESEARCHING

Have students create new foldables titled Prenatal Care and label the tabs Importance of Care, Proper Nutrition, Health of the Fetus, and Complications. Have them use the foldables to record main ideas. Discuss with students how

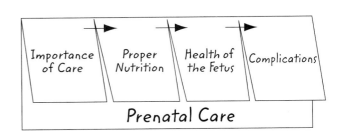

more and more surgery is being done on babies still in the womb to remedy birth defects and other problems. A tiny transmitter can be implanted in the mother's womb to monitor the health of the fetus afterward. Ask interested students to do some research on this technology and report their findings to the class.

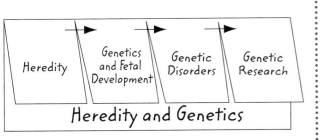

DRAWING CONCLUSIONS

Have students create new foldables titled Heredity and Genetics. They should label the tabs Heredity, Genetics and Fetal Development, Genetic Disorders, and Genetic Research. Have them write the main ideas under the tabs. Organize a roundtable or panel discussion on the topic of "designer" babies, children whose eye color, intelligence, and other characteristics might be manipulated with genetic engineering. Would this be desirable or not?

Student Study Tip

Discuss with the class ways in which they can improve their concentration, enabling them to study more efficiently and with better results. Suggest that they study in the same spot every day so they will learn to associate that spot with focusing on schoolwork. Although some students claim they concentrate best when music is playing, studies show this is usually a false impression. Quiet works best. Also, they should prioritize tasks and focus on only one task at a time.

Chapter 19

FOLDABLES

Adolescence and the Life Cycle

CHAPTER SUMMARY

Adolescence is a period of rapid growth. As young people move toward adulthood, most reach physical maturity. Emotional maturity is reached when the person's mental and emotional capabilities are realized. These capabilities involve establishing intimate relationships. Marriage is a long-term commitment between two people who decide to spend the rest of their lives together. Middle adulthood is a time of transition. Late adulthood is the final stage of development.

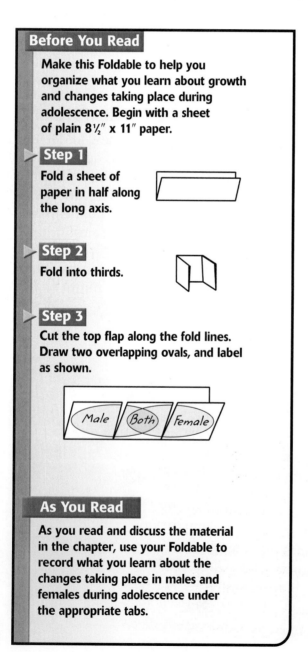

Before You Read

Make this Foldable to help you organize what you learn about growth and changes taking place during adolescence. Begin with a sheet of plain 8½" x 11" paper.

Step 1

Fold a sheet of paper in half along the long axis.

Step 2

Fold into thirds.

Step 3

Cut the top flap along the fold lines. Draw two overlapping ovals, and label as shown.

Male *Both* *Female*

As You Read

As you read and discuss the material in the chapter, use your Foldable to record what you learn about the changes taking place in males and females during adolescence under the appropriate tabs.

CHAPTER REVIEW

Foldables Follow-Up Activity

Discuss with students the concept of a rite of passage in which the individual is given symbolic aid and social support at different turning points in life, such as adolescence. Industrialized cultures seem to have fewer of these rituals than more traditional cultures. Is this a positive trend or not?

TEACHER NOTES

_____
_____
_____
_____
_____
_____
_____
_____
_____
_____
_____
_____
_____
_____
_____

Alternative Activities for Chapter 20

DISCUSSING

Have students create new foldables and label the outer tabs Marriage and Parenting and the middle tab Both. Have them write under the tabs the factors in successful marriage and parenting and those they share. Divide the class into small groups to discuss whether or not state regulations should make it more difficult for people to marry, including requiring such things as a long waiting period and evidence of financial responsibility.

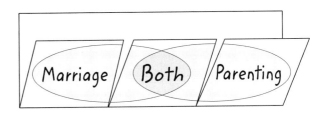

ANALYZING

Have students make new foldables and label the outer tabs Middle Adulthood and Late Adulthood and the middle tab Both. Have them write under the tabs the transitions that apply to each and those they share. Ask a representative from a nursing home or assisted living residence to speak to the class about a typical day at the facility. Have students prepare questions in advance. Later, brainstorm with the class ways for older adults to remain an active part of the community.

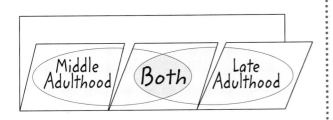

Student Study Tip

Some students may be slow readers because of poor vocabulary. Suggest they improve their vocabulary by reading more. To ensure motivation, have them at first select subjects they are especially interested in. Encourage them to stop and learn the meaning of new words rather than skipping over them. Suggest they keep vocabulary notebooks and have a pocket dictionary on hand.

Chapter 20

FOLDABLES

Tobacco

CHAPTER SUMMARY

All forms of tobacco involve health risks. Tobacco is the number-one cause of preventable disease in the U.S. Tobacco use harms the nervous, digestive, respiratory, cardiovascular, and excretory systems. Tobacco use has declined among teens. People who are trying to give up tobacco can use several strategies. Environmental tobacco smoke is composed of mainstream smoke and sidestream smoke. Both types have harmful effects on nonsmokers. Teens can help work toward a smoke-free society.

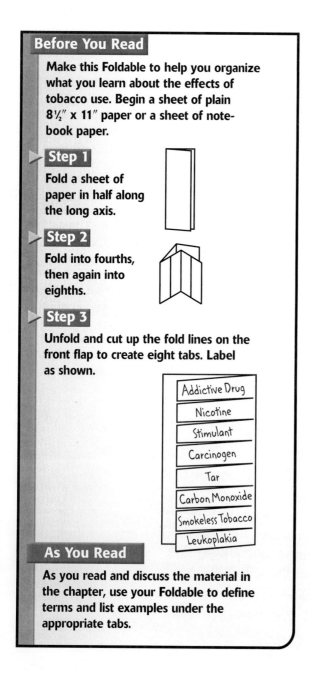

Before You Read

Make this Foldable to help you organize what you learn about the effects of tobacco use. Begin a sheet of plain 8½″ x 11″ paper or a sheet of notebook paper.

Step 1

Fold a sheet of paper in half along the long axis.

Step 2

Fold into fourths, then again into eighths.

Step 3

Unfold and cut up the fold lines on the front flap to create eight tabs. Label as shown.

Addictive Drug
Nicotine
Stimulant
Carcinogen
Tar
Carbon Monoxide
Smokeless Tobacco
Leukoplakia

As You Read

As you read and discuss the material in the chapter, use your Foldable to define terms and list examples under the appropriate tabs.

CHAPTER REVIEW

Foldables Follow-Up Activity

Have students research and write a report or make a multimedia presentation on the history of tobacco use. What was its initial purpose? When did it become widely used and when was information about health concerns first made widely available in the U.S.?

TEACHER NOTES

_____
_____
_____
_____
_____
_____
_____
_____
_____
_____
_____
_____
_____
_____
_____

Alternative Activities for Chapter 21

MAKING A SURVEY

Have students create new foldables. Title the top tab Tips for Quitting, label the next six tabs with the tips, and label the last tab Withdrawal. Have them record main ideas under the tabs. Have students survey three adults and three teens about whether they have ever smoked and, if so, whether they have ever tried to quit. Were they successful? Have the class graph the results.

| Tips for Quitting |
| Prepare for the Day |
| Get Support and Encouragement |
| Identify Services |
| Healthier Alternatives |
| Change Daily Behavior |
| Engage in Healthful Behaviors |
| Withdrawal |

| Environmental Tobacco Smoke |
| Mainstream Smoke |
| Sidestream Smoke |
| Effects on Unborn Children |
| Effects on Young Children |
| Reducing Risks |
| Smoke-free Society |
| National Health Goals |

INTERVIEWING

Have students create new foldables and write environmental tobacco smoke, mainstream smoke, sidestream smoke, effects on unborn children, effects on young children, reducing risks, smoke-free society, and national health goals on the tabs. Have them record main ideas and definitions under the tabs. If possible, ask a physician to talk to the class about the link between smoking and diseases such as lung cancer. Have the class prepare questions in advance.

Student Study Tip

Students will find written reports easier to complete successfully if they make sure they are clear about the subject, the format, the writing style, the required number of pages, and the date the report is due. Writing a topic statement describing what the report will be about is helpful in establishing their focus. Encourage them to make as many drafts as necessary to make sure the report is clear and that grammar and spelling are correct. If possible, they should ask someone else to read the report and flag any errors or ideas that need clarifying.

Chapter 21

FOLDABLES

Alcohol

CHAPTER SUMMARY

Alcohol is an addictive drug that poses risks to health. Peer pressure, family, and media messages all influence alcohol use. Many teens make the commitment to stay alcohol free. Alcohol has short-term effects on the nervous, cardiovascular, digestive, and respiratory systems. Driving under the influence of alcohol is the leading cause of death among teens. Alcohol also has long-term effects on the brain, the cardiovascular system, the liver, the digestive system, and the pancreas. It has many negative effects on families and society.

Before You Read

Make this Foldable to help you organize what you learn about alcohol and about choosing to be alcohol free. Begin with four sheets of 8½" x 11" paper or four sheets of notebook paper.

Step 1

Fold four sheets of paper in half along the short axis.

Step 2

On each sheet, make a cut 1" from the edge of the paper. Cut through the top flap only.

Step 3

Staple the four sheets together at the 1" tabs and label them: The Facts About Alcohol, Factors That Influence Alcohol Use, Avoid Alcohol: Avoid Unsafe Situations, and Being Alcohol Free.

The Facts About Alcohol

As You Read

As you read and discuss the material in the chapter, use your Foldable to define terms and record what you learn under the appropriate tabs.

CHAPTER REVIEW

Foldables Follow-Up Activity

Divide the class into small groups and ask each group to write a radio commercial for choosing to be alcohol free. Have the groups perform and tape their commercials and arrange for them to be broadcast over the school public address system or at a school event.

TEACHER NOTES

Alternative Activities for Chapter 22

DRAWING CONCLUSIONS

Have students make new foldables and label them Alcohol and Drug Interactions, Driving Under the Influence, Binge Drinking, and Alcohol Poisoning Use the foldables to record main ideas. Write the following on the chalkboard: "The sale of alcohol should/should not be made illegal in the U.S." Then ask students to take a position on the topic and write a paragraph explaining their reasons. Discuss what happened during Prohibition (1919–1933). Ask students to find out why it was finally repealed.

SHARING INFORMATION

Have students make new foldables and label them Alcoholics, Factors Affecting Alcoholism, Stages of Alcoholism, and Effects on Family and Society. They can use the foldables to record main ideas. Arrange with teachers from other schools in your county or state to set up a telecollaborative project in which students create a database of treatment options, support groups, advocacy groups, and other resources for teens and their families.

Student Study Tip

Review with students ways in which to get the most help from a dictionary. Point out where pronunciations and variant spellings are found in the entries. Remind them where the pronunciation key is located. Warn them about homographs—words that have the same spelling but different meanings. Are homographs listed under a single entry or in separate entries? Point out word origins and prefixes and suffixes, which may be useful in helping them understand or remember the meaning of a word.

Medicines and Drugs

CHAPTER SUMMARY

Medicines may be classified into four main groups. These include those that fight pathogens, those that relieve pain, and those that promote health. Substance abuse is any unnecessary or improper use of chemical substances for non-medical purposes. Drug abuse has consequences for the individual, for family and friends, for babies and children, and for society. Marijuana is harmful in itself and can lead to the use of other drugs. Inhalants cause mind-altering effects. Psychoactive drugs include stimulants, depressants, narcotics, and hallucinogens. They affect the central nervous system. Teens can use refusal skills to stay drug free.

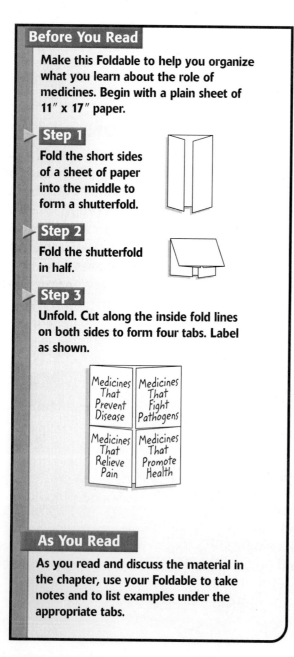

Before You Read

Make this Foldable to help you organize what you learn about the role of medicines. Begin with a plain sheet of 11″ x 17″ paper.

Step 1

Fold the short sides of a sheet of paper into the middle to form a shutterfold.

Step 2

Fold the shutterfold in half.

Step 3

Unfold. Cut along the inside fold lines on both sides to form four tabs. Label as shown.

Medicines That Prevent Disease | Medicines That Fight Pathogens
Medicines That Relieve Pain | Medicines That Promote Health

As You Read

As you read and discuss the material in the chapter, use your Foldable to take notes and to list examples under the appropriate tabs.

CHAPTER REVIEW

Foldables Follow-Up Activity

Acquaint students with online medical sites such as WebMD or the Merck Manual. Ask them to analyze the information available on prescription drugs. Does it seem reliable? Does the site accept advertising? If so, how might that have either a positive or negative influence on the site?

TEACHER NOTES

_____
_____
_____
_____
_____
_____
_____
_____
_____
_____
_____
_____
_____

Alternative Activities for Chapter 23

INTERVIEWING

Have students create new foldables and label the tabs Marijuana, Inhalants, Steroids, and Psychoactive Drugs. Notes can be made under the tabs. Arrange for the class to have an online chat with an expert on drug abuse. Ask students to prepare questions for the expert in advance based on what they've learned in this chapter.

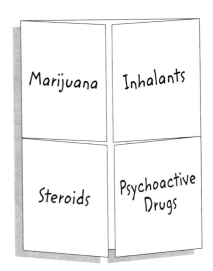

ANALYZING

Have students make new foldables and label the tabs Resisting Pressure to Use Drugs, Efforts to Curb Drug Abuse, Becoming Drug Free, and Getting Help. They should record main ideas under the tabs. After previewing it yourself for appropriateness, ask students to watch a film on recovering from drug abuse, such as *28 Days* with Sandra Bullock. Ask them to analyze the main character's motivations in using drugs. Do self-absorption or escape from perceived problems play a part? Is the character attractive while high? Why or why not?

Student Study Tip

Remind students of the SQ3R method for improving reading comprehension and memory. S stands for *survey*, which means to preview the material by looking at such things as the title, headings, and illustrations. Q stands for *questions*. Students should read end-of-chapter and other questions for clues as to what kinds of information they should be looking for. 3R stands for *read*, *recite*, and *review*. They should read the material, recite the answers to the questions, and review the answers again later to keep the information fresh in their minds.

Chapter 23

FOLDABLES

Communicable Diseases

CHAPTER SUMMARY

Pathogens spread communicable diseases. Direct contact, indirect contact, and airborne transmission transmit these diseases. Washing hands, handling food properly, and other preventive measures help prevent the spread of disease. Physical and chemical barriers prevent pathogens from entering the body. The immune system works to overcome invading pathogens. Vaccines aid the body's defenses. Common communicable diseases include respiratory infections, hepatitis, and emerging infections, among others.

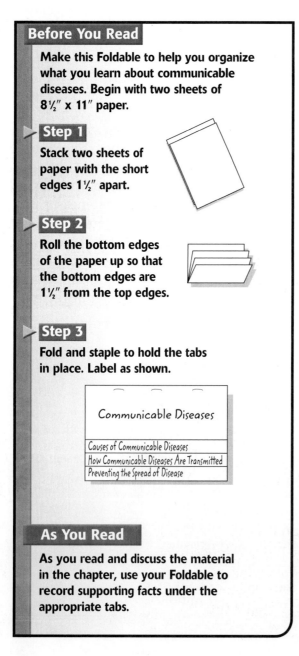

Before You Read

Make this Foldable to help you organize what you learn about communicable diseases. Begin with two sheets of 8½″ x 11″ paper.

Step 1

Stack two sheets of paper with the short edges 1½″ apart.

Step 2

Roll the bottom edges of the paper up so that the bottom edges are 1½″ from the top edges.

Step 3

Fold and staple to hold the tabs in place. Label as shown.

Communicable Diseases

Causes of Communicable Diseases
How Communicable Diseases Are Transmitted
Preventing the Spread of Disease

As You Read

As you read and discuss the material in the chapter, use your Foldable to record supporting facts under the appropriate tabs.

CHAPTER REVIEW

Foldables Follow-Up Activity

Discuss with students how Edward Jenner first tested his smallpox vaccine on an eight-year-old boy by exposing the boy to the pathogen. Compare his method to how long the FDA approval process takes for a new drug today and what steps are involved. Hold a panel discussion on whether or not Jenner's type of trial would be acceptable today and if the current process should be accelerated.

TEACHER NOTES

_____
_____
_____
_____
_____
_____
_____
_____
_____
_____

Alternative Activities for Chapter 24

INVESTIGATING

Have students create new foldables titled The Immune System and label the tabs Inflammatory Response, Specific Defenses, and Memory Lymphocytes. Have them record main ideas under the tabs. Ask volunteers to read *Anatomy of an Illness* by Norman Cousins, in which the author chronicles his recovery from a life-threatening disease using laughter, and report on Cousins' methods to the class. Discuss Cousins' hypothesis that laughter stimulates the immune system and encourages healing. Ask students to devise a test and conduct a study of Cousins' method. Ask them to determine what effects, if any, it might have on the subject's mental/emotional health.

> *The Immune System*
>
> Inflammatory Response
> Specific Defenses
> Memory Lymphocytes

EVALUATING

Have students create new foldables titled Common Communicable Diseases and label the tabs Respiratory Infections, Hepatitis, and Emerging Infections. Have them make notes under the tabs. Discuss how polio was once a serious threat and show photographs of the iron lungs used to keep patients alive. Today polio seems gone for good, but is it? Other "vanquished" diseases, like tuberculosis have recently reappeared. Have students do some research about polio and write a short paper giving their opinion as to the danger of recurrence and backing it up with facts.

> *Common Communicable Diseases*
>
> Respiratory Infections
> Hepatitis
> Emerging Infections

Student Study Tip

Students may often be called upon to write formal letters or e-mails. Give them these tips: 1) Before you begin, think about what you want to say and to whom you want to say it. If necessary, make notes. 2) Write a rough draft of the letter or e-mail. In the first paragraph, state your purpose in writing. In following paragraphs, go into necessary details. In the last paragraph, state what, if anything, you would like to have done. 3) Rewrite the letter as needed to make it clear and accurate. 4) Proof the letter for grammar and spelling. Be sure names and addresses are accurate. 5) Make a neat final draft.

Chapter 24

FOLDABLES

Sexually Transmitted Infections and HIV/AIDS

CHAPTER SUMMARY

STDs are associated with high-risk behaviors. The only sure method of preventing them is abstinence. Common STDs include human papillomavirus, chlamydia, genital herpes, gonorrhea, trichomoniasis, and syphilis. HIV attacks the immune system. Its latter stage of development is called AIDS. AIDS is now pandemic. Abstinence and avoiding risk behaviors are the best ways to avoid AIDS.

Before You Read

Make this Foldable to help you organize what you learn about the risks of sexually transmitted infections. Begin with a sheet of 8½" x 11" paper.

Step 1

Fold a sheet of paper along the long axis so the bottom edge lies 2" from the top edge.

Step 2

Fold into thirds.

Step 3

Unfold and cut along the inside fold lines. Label as shown.

THE RISKS OF STDs

Behaviors | Consequences | Prevention

As You Read

As you read and discuss the material in the chapter, use your Foldable to define terms and record what you learn.

CHAPTER REVIEW

Foldables Follow-Up Activity

If students are publishing an e-zine, ask them to add material to it about preventing the spread of STIs and include links to other relevant sites. If they have not created an e-zine, have them distribute leaflets recommending prevention methods throughout the school.

TEACHER NOTES

_____
_____
_____
_____
_____
_____
_____
_____
_____
_____
_____
_____
_____
_____

Alternative Activities for Chapter 25

COMPARING DATA

Have students make new foldables titled HIV and AIDS; label the tabs Teens at Risk, HIV and the Body, and Transmission. They can make notes and define terms under the tabs. Have interested students research AIDS statistics for at least five other countries and prepare a graph for comparison. What are some possible reasons for differences in numbers of infected people?

HIV and AIDS

Teens at Risk | Transmission | HIV and the Body

COMPILING INFORMATION

Have students make new foldables titled Treatment and label the tabs Stages of HIV Infection, Detecting HIV, and Research and Treatment. Have them make notes and define terms under the tabs. Have students compile a list of organizations in their community a person could contact for confidential testing for AIDS or support for those who have the disease. Encourage students to organize a community fund-raising event for AIDS research.

Treatment

Stages of HIV Infection | Detecting HIV | Research and Treatment

Student Study Tip

Remind students not to rely completely on their computer's spell checker. Words can be spelled correctly and still be terribly wrong. For fun, write the following poem on the chalkboard and ask students to correct the errors:

Eye halve a spell chequer.
It came with my pea sea.
It plane lea marques four my revue
Miss steaks eye kin knot sea.

Eye halve run this poem threw it,
And, I'm shore your pleased two no,
Its letter perfect awl the weigh—
My chequer tolled me sew.

Chapter 25

FOLDABLES

Noncommunicable Diseases and Disabilities

CHAPTER SUMMARY

Cardiovascular diseases include hypertension, atherosclerosis, diseases of the heart, and stroke. Behaviors established during the teen years and early adulthood can influence a person's risk. Cancer is the uncontrollable growth of abnormal cells. A person can reduce the risk of cancer by practicing healthful behaviors. Chronic noncommunicable diseases include allergies, asthma, diabetes, and arthritis. A disability is any physical or mental impairment that limits normal activities.

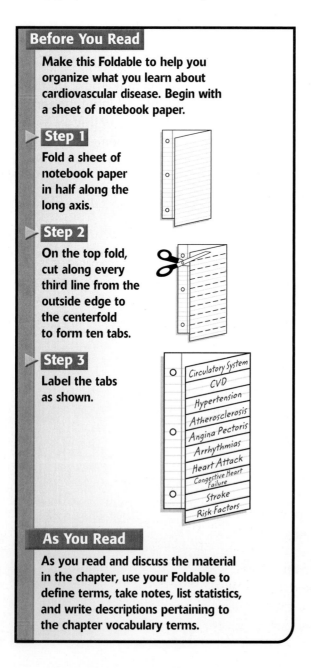

Before You Read

Make this Foldable to help you organize what you learn about cardiovascular disease. Begin with a sheet of notebook paper.

Step 1

Fold a sheet of notebook paper in half along the long axis.

Step 2

On the top fold, cut along every third line from the outside edge to the centerfold to form ten tabs.

Step 3

Label the tabs as shown.

Circulatory System
CVD
Hypertension
Atherosclerosis
Angina Pectoris
Arrhythmias
Heart Attack
Congestive Heart Failure
Stroke
Risk Factors

As You Read

As you read and discuss the material in the chapter, use your Foldable to define terms, take notes, list statistics, and write descriptions pertaining to the chapter vocabulary terms.

CHAPTER REVIEW

Foldables Follow-Up Activity

Students may be interested in learning more about the first FDA-approved surgical robot used for heart bypass operations. Developed at the Ohio State University Medical Center, the robot has performed more than 3,000 open-heart surgeries. Discuss whether or not students would want to be operated on by a robot and why.

TEACHER NOTES

_____
_____
_____
_____
_____
_____
_____
_____
_____
_____
_____
_____
_____

Alternative Activities for Chapter 26

ADVOCACY

Have students make new foldables and write cancer, tumor, benign, malignant, metastasis, carcinogen, biopsy, remission, types of cancer, and risk factors on the tabs. Have them use the foldable to define terms and make notes. Encourage students to participate in a fund-raising event for cancer, such as the Race for the Cure, or to contact a local support group and organize their own community event.

Cancer
Tumor
Benign
Malignant
Metastasis
Carcinogen
Biopsy
Remission
Types of Cancer
Risk Factors

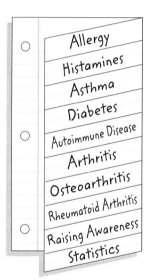

Allergy
Histamines
Asthma
Diabetes
Autoimmune Disease
Arthritis
Osteoarthritis
Rheumatoid Arthritis
Raising Awareness
Statistics

RESEARCHING

Have students make new foldables and label the tabs allergy, histamines, asthma, diabetes, autoimmune disease, arthritis, osteoarthritis, rheumatoid arthritis, raising awareness, and statistics. Have them use the foldables to define terms and make notes. Have students research "orphan" diseases, those that do not afflict enough people to make finding a cure profitable for pharmaceutical companies. Ask students to write a report on the problem and make recommendations for what might be done.

Student Study Tip

Some students may need help when they try to summarize a passage. Suggest that they first make a list of the main ideas. Next, they should identify the important details by asking who, what, when, where, why, and how. They should then write the summary in their own words. Remind them that a summary is shorter than the original material. It *sums up* the original.

Chapter 26

FOLDABLES

Injury Prevention and Safe Behaviors

CHAPTER SUMMARY

The accident chain is a sequence of events that can lead to unintentional injury. Steps can be taken to prevent fires, falls, electrical shock, poisoning and firearm injuries. Recreational activities can lead to injuries if safety precautions are not followed. Motor vehicle crashes are the leading cause of death among teens. Severe weather includes hurricanes, floods, thunderstorms, tornadoes, and winter storms. Earthquakes, too, can cause many casualties. Preparing an emergency survival kit can be helpful.

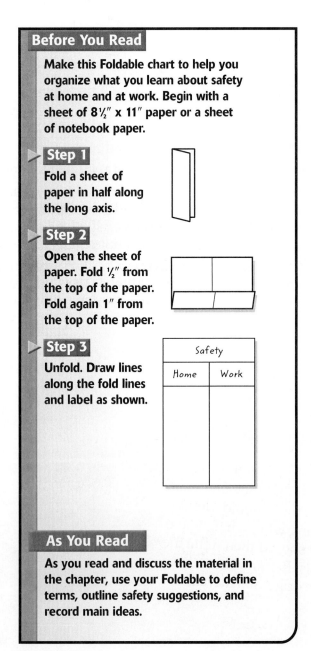

Before You Read

Make this Foldable chart to help you organize what you learn about safety at home and at work. Begin with a sheet of 8½" x 11" paper or a sheet of notebook paper.

Step 1

Fold a sheet of paper in half along the long axis.

Step 2

Open the sheet of paper. Fold ½" from the top of the paper. Fold again 1" from the top of the paper.

Step 3

Unfold. Draw lines along the fold lines and label as shown.

Safety	
Home	Work

As You Read

As you read and discuss the material in the chapter, use your Foldable to define terms, outline safety suggestions, and record main ideas.

CHAPTER REVIEW

Foldables Follow-Up Activity

Divide the class into small groups. Ask students to discuss the information in their foldables in relation to accidents they've had or nearly had. What was the unsafe situation or action? What could have been done to prevent the accident?

TEACHER NOTES

_____

_____

_____

_____

_____

_____

_____

_____

_____

_____

_____

_____

_____

Alternative Activities for Chapter 27

EVALUATING

Have students create new foldables titled Safety on the Road and label the columns Automobile Safety and Safety on Wheels. Have them define terms and record main ideas in the appropriate columns. Discuss with the class event data recorders, "black boxes" for recording data on car operations, which are installed in all cars with airbags. The data collected can help determine the cause of an accident and have been used against drivers in court. Consumer models are available for parents who want to monitor teen drivers. Do students think the devices are a good idea or not?

Safety on the Road	
Automobile Safety	Safety on the Road

Weather Emergencies and Natural Disasters	
Severe Weather	Earthquakes

DRAWING CONCLUSIONS

Have students create new foldables labeled Weather Emergencies and Natural Disasters and label the columns Severe Weather and Earthquakes. Have them define terms and make notes in the appropriate columns. Show the class a video about storm trackers and discuss their contribution to scientific knowledge about how storms evolve. How can this improve general safety?

Student Study Tip

Some students become nervous when asked to make a presentation. Provide them with the following tips to help them prepare. 1) Evaluate your audience. How much do they already know about your subject? 2) Prepare an outline of the information you want to cover. Give background information or an overview first. 3) If applicable, plan to give a demonstration of some kind. It will help your audience understand better. 4) At the end, summarize your main points. 5) When you've finished, ask for questions.

Chapter 27 **FOLDABLES**

First Aid and Emergencies

CHAPTER SUMMARY

First aid is the immediate temporary care given to a person who is ill or injured until professional medical care arrives. Different problems involve different types of care. CPR combines rescue breaths with chest compression to aid breathing and heartbeat. CPR for infants and children differs from that for adults. Common emergencies include muscle, joint, and bone injuries; unconsciousness; animal bites; nosebleeds; and an object in the eye. Poison may enter the body through swallowing, inhalation, skin contact, insect stings, and animal bites.

Before You Read

Make this Foldable to help you organize what you learn about providing first aid. Begin with a sheet of 8½" x 11" paper or notebook paper.

Step 1

Fold a sheet of paper in half along the long axis.

Step 2

Fold into thirds.

Step 3

Cut the top layer along both folds. Label as shown.

Check | Call | Care

As You Read

As you read and discuss the material in the chapter, use your Foldable to record what you learn about the three Cs, the first steps to take in an emergency situation.

CHAPTER REVIEW

Foldables Follow-Up Activity

Discuss with students how wars often speed the development of inventions and innovations. Ask volunteers to find out if any new methods for treating injuries were developed for use in the wars in Afghanistan and Iraq. Acquaint students with how Florence Nightingale established nursing as a profession for women during the Crimean War.

TEACHER NOTES

_____

_____

_____

_____

_____

_____

_____

_____

_____

_____

_____

Alternative Activities for Chapter 28

IDENTIFYING

Have students make new foldables and label the tabs Airway, Breathing, and Circulation. Have them record main ideas under the tabs. Some communities are debating whether or not to keep defibrillators in public buildings for use in emergencies. Ask volunteers to find out if they are being made available in your community and where.

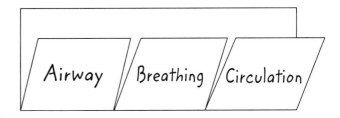

EVALUATING

Have students make new foldables and label the tabs Muscle Cramps, Strains and Sprains, and Fractures and Dislocations. Have them record main ideas under the tabs. Divide the class into small groups and ask each group to evaluate a consumer product used for wounds and other injuries, such as bandages that accelerate healing or reduce scarring. Does the product work as promised?

Muscle Cramps / Strains and Sprains / Fractures and Dislocations

Student Study Tip

Some students may find it difficult to remember information. Write the following tips on the chalkboard: 1) Connect the new information to what you already know about the subject. 2) Repeat the information by reciting it or writing it down. 3) Use memory tricks, such as songs or short poems that give clues, such as "I before E except after C." 4) When applicable, form a mental picture of some kind related to the information.

Chapter 28 **FOLDABLES**

Environmental Health

CHAPTER SUMMARY

Air pollution is the contamination of the atmosphere by substances that pose a health threat. Both indoor and outdoor air may be polluted. Noise pollution is harmful and unwanted sound that can damage hearing. Solid or hazardous wastes may contaminate land and water. Steps can be taken to reduce land and water pollution. Everyone can help the environment by conserving resources and precycling and recycling. Teens can also help by becoming informed consumers, contacting organizations that work on environmental issues, and taking action against local polluters.

Before You Read

Make this Foldable study guide to record and collect information on air quality and types of pollution. Begin with a sheet of 11" x 17" paper.

Step 1

Fold a sheet of paper into thirds.

Step 2

Unfold. Fold 2" of the bottom side of the paper upward. Glue or staple the sides of the fold to form pockets.

Step 3

Label as shown. Place 3" x 5" notecards or pieces of paper inside the pockets.

Air Pollution	Indoor Air Pollution	Noise Pollution

As You Read

As you read and discuss the material in the chapter, use your Foldable to record and define terms, identify and explain each type of pollution, and list possible causes and effects.

CHAPTER REVIEW

Foldables Follow-Up Activity

Have students investigate the pollution caused by artificial lights left on all night long, especially in cities. How does this type of pollution affect animal behavior, human biorhythms, and mental/emotional health? Could it be related in any way to increased health problems among third-shift workers? Are humans more intimately connected to nature's cycles than is ordinarily thought?

TEACHER NOTES

_____
_____
_____
_____
_____
_____
_____
_____
_____
_____
_____
_____

Alternative Activities for Chapter 29

INTERVIEWING

Have students make new foldables and label the pockets Waste Disposal, Expansion and Development, and Water Supplies and Pollution. Students can use the foldables to hold study cards. Then have them interview an older adult who has lived in the area most of her or his life and ask how the area has changed in terms of the topics in their foldables. Ask students to write an article about the interview for the school paper or their health e-zine.

Waste Disposal	Expansion and Development	Water Supplies and Pollution

Conserving Resources	Precycling and Recycling	Protecting the Environment

INVESTIGATING

Have students make new foldables and label the pockets Conserving Resources, Precycling and Recycling, and Protecting the Environment. They can use the foldables to hold study cards. Have students investigate biosphere projects in which people lived within a sealed environment for a period of time. What provisions were made for air quality, food, water, waste disposal, and living quarters? What was the purpose of the project and was it successful?

Student Study Tip

Suggest the following tips to students for taking a test: Quickly skim the entire test and read directions before beginning. Ask the instructor to explain anything that is not clear. Answer the easiest questions first; then you'll know how much time is left for harder questions. When answering an essay question, be sure you read the directions carefully. What are you being asked to do: explain, compare, discuss, list, or describe? Then be sure you do what is asked. Don't worry if others in the room finish before you do; focus just on your own task. When you finish, check your answers.

FOLDABLES